A PRIEST
CONFESSES

A PRIEST CONFESSES

by José Luis Martín Descalzo

Translated by Rita Goldberg

ACADEMY GUILD PRESS

LIBRARY OF CONGRESS CATALOG CARD NUMBER: 60—14624

COPYRIGHT © 1960 BY ACADEMY LIBRARY GUILD

First American Edition

Originally published in Spanish as *Un cura se confiesa*
by Juan Flors, Editor, Barcelona, in 1956

MANUFACTURED IN THE UNITED STATES OF AMERICA
TYPOGRAPHY: PACIFIC LINOTYPING COMPANY
LITHOGRAPHY: SIERRA PRINTING AND LITHOGRAPH COMPANY
BINDING: INLAND BINDERY
ALL OF FRESNO, CALIFORNIA

DEDICATION

This book has not been written for you,
known and unknown priests of Spain and
of the world. However, I want this
dedication to be for you because you
are the only ones who can understand
that these pages do not come from my
imagination.

CONTENTS

A PRIEST
CONFESSES

A QUEER BIRD

I HAD JUST LEFT ONE OF THOSE LITTLE BASQUE trains that go through fields which give the impression of always being newly painted. It had rained and a strong smell of wet earth penetrated everything. I felt happy without knowing exactly why. Perhaps for the sake of accompanying the countryside in its joy.

As I had an hour between trains—I was to catch the eight o'clock express for Madrid—I went to take a stroll through the town. It seemed small to me. It was virtually only one, rather long street which went from the station to the church. I began to walk down it. Many boys on bicycles passed by, shouting to each other.

The church was almost deserted; there were only two girls kneeling together in one of the first pews and an old woman on a prie-dieu. I sat down at the back of the church. It felt good there. My eyes, my ears and my soul rested in the cool half-light. It was easy for me to pray. My life has never been filled with complications and for me praying is simply speaking with He Who is in the Tabernacle. So it was that we chatted a while and then—without realizing it—my mind wandered and I began to think that I was going home. I smiled. Yes, there were reasons for being happy. Two years far from the family and now I was going back for three months, three months of leave, as soldiers say. I remembered the four days I had spent in Loyola with my sister. The habit was becoming to her, although it made her look older. She was very happy and this was the most important thing. Her eyes were gayer than ever. I remembered that we had spent more than half the time telling jokes, jokes that she jotted down in a little notebook in order to tell them to the other novices at recreation. "I have such a bad memory," she said to me, "that in half an hour I won't remember any of them." No, she wasn't maudlin. She spoke as naturally as before, but, if possible, more so, because she said even the most serious and tremendous things in a delicious, naïve tone. We talked of everything: what they were given to eat, the apple trees that crowded their garden, their hours of prayer, their Masses. And she told it to me, stressing it all equally. And I assure you that the name of God sounded better in the same tone that she used to say, for example, "apple". It sounded more natural and more within reach.

I was bemused thinking about these things and had not noticed that one of the girls who were kneeling in front had come towards me.

"Father, could you hear our confession?"

I was a little bewildered.

"Oh," I said. "I'm not a priest yet. I'm a seminarian."

She blushed and went off, effusively begging my pardon.

This little anecdote was very funny to me. It would have been a fine thing for me to have turned solemn and heard their confession. But you can't play around or fool with these things. I pushed aside the thought as a temptation, but the truth is that I was delighted by the fact that they had taken me for a priest. I thought:

"Can my face already be that of a serious person?"

And I put my hand to my cheek.

"Of course. I haven't shaved for two days . . . I'll go to a barber right now."

With no further ado, I got up and, without saying a word of farewell to God, I went towards the door. On taking holy water from the font, I realized how discourteous I had been and, from there, laughing, I said to Him:

"Forgive me. I'm a fool. You understand."

When I left the barber shop—with my face younger now—I started off towards the station because it was getting to be time. I felt hungry and said to myself:

"I'll have to buy something for supper. I don't get in until two o'clock."

I went into one of those shops which look like they sell everything and, before I had really thought out what I wanted, said:

"A hundred grams of sausage."

The woman must have seen it in my face, for she said to me:

"Is it for a sandwich?"

"Yes."

"Fifty are enough for you."

"All right. Give me fifty. I said a hundred grams simply to say something."

She sliced it for me.

"Do you want bread?"

"Oh, do you sell it here, too? So much the better. Yes, please give me some."

"Shall I make the sandwich for you?"

"Yes, please."

"Do you want some fruit?"

"Yes, give me some."

"Two bananas?"

"Fine."

"No. Better one banana and a pear. Some cookies?"

"All right."

"Four?"

"Yes."

6

I let her take over. She felt a little as though she were my mother and I didn't have the slightest idea of how much she was going to charge. I have never paid much attention to what I eat. The woman in the store must have thought it a wonderful thing to wait on a person who was so easy to please and she rewarded my complaisance by fondly preparing the package for me. Almost as if my mother had done it.

With the package containing my supper as my only baggage—I had checked the rest of it through from Irún—I got on the express. It was quite crowded but I found a seat.

My compartment was one of those it is easy to find on the express from Irún. Next to the window there was an Italian couple, either engaged or newly-weds, who spent the entire trip doing crossword puzzles together. In front of them, a couple from Valencia who ate sausage for two hours, spoke Valencian for another two, and devoured cheese for another two. Together, also.

The remaining six of us formed the only other group. In front of me, two English boys and a Spanish girl who had lived in England from the time she was a child. To my right, a Spaniard who looked as though he might be a shoemaker and who was returning to Spain after seventeen years in France; and to my left, a boy of about twenty-five, well-dressed, who, I later learned, was an engineering student. And I, who sat almost exactly in front of the Spanish-English girl. She wore quite ordinary clothes and had on absolutely no makeup. She was pale and all her hair was pulled back in a pony-tail.

We conversed laboriously in French (the only one who spoke it well was my neighbor to the right), but this was the only way of not leaving out the two English boys who also managed to muddle through in French. And we could always resort to the girl who spoke to them in French and to us in Spanish, an almost perfect Spanish which she pronounced very gently and which had a faint dictionary air about it.

But, almost imperceptibly, the conversation shifted from French to Spanish and we ended up neglecting the two English boys who shut themselves up in their thoughts. The subject of our conversation was the usual one among people who are returning from abroad: Spanish trains.

"Still, it can't be denied that we are improving. This train we are riding on now isn't half bad."

"No, of course. There is an indisputable improvement in many things. It's always nice to come and find new things."

While I was saying this, I put my hand in my pocket to take out my handkerchief and happened on something cold: a coin.

I took it out and said:

"Duros*, for example."

And, suddenly changing the subject, I went on:

"Why just yesterday a strange thing happened to me with them. I am on my way from Loyola where a sister of mine is a nun, and the other day, very intrigued, she asked me if there were silver duros already. Apparently

---

* Duro: a Spanish five peseta coin, worth about $.08. R.G.

they had argued a bit about it at recreation, because one of the novices who had just entered the convent said that she had seen them and the others said that there hadn't been any since the war."

"A sister of yours is a nun?" asked the girl who was facing me.

"Yes, she is a novice. Here, in Loyola."

"Two of my aunts in England are nuns. In fact . . . "

She stopped as if she had repented of what she was going to say. But she continued:

"I don't want to annoy you, but whenever I go to visit them they make me feel sorry."

"Sorry?"

"Yes, they speak from another world, like people who are different from the rest of us. They were just children when they went into the convent and they have no idea what the world is like. They don't speak our language; they don't understand us at all. The world goes on and they are dead."

"But they are happy."

"They are happy because they don't know any better. They are like children who have a glass of water and think they have all the water in the world because they haven't seen more. I'm sorry for them, I tell you. They know nothing about life. And they are not happy; they only think they are. Whenever I go to see them I am very sad when I leave. There, always shut up, their lives seem lost, useless to me."

"That depends on what you mean by 'life'."

"Life is this," and she held out her arms as if not

knowing how to explain herself. "Life is all this that there is before our eyes. Why do they become nuns? I have never been able to understand it. I think that it is out of fear or because they are naïve. Anyway, they always seem strange, torn away from everything."

The subject hurt me and she realized it. That is why she stopped and I did not ask the question that was on my lips: Then you most likely don't understand why I am becoming a priest? There was an embarrassed silence. In the compartment, everyone was listening to us now. I should have given an answer, said the word that was needed. But I felt sad. I spoke of the other life, of true life. But I must have done it like someone quoting a book, as though reciting it by heart.

It had grown dark, and beyond the windows, in the aisle, I sought that countryside which a few short hours before had filled me with joy. It wasn't there.

Neither was there joy in my heart, and I felt grey dejection, secret rage, a strange desire to cry.

The train was traveling fast, leaving behind the tremulous little lights of the towns lost in the night, and, as we approached Castile, more stars began to be seen in the sky. I rested my chin on the nickel bar that crossed the window and repeated angrily—chewing them—the words I had said to the girl.

Yes, I was a strange one, a queer bird who had cropped up from another world. I had nothing to do with all those men who were in the train. My cassock was like a pneumatic bell which would gradually pump out my heart.

10

Why did it have to be that way? They knew perfectly well that we weren't different, that our flesh was the same as theirs, that we had the same passions, the same idiosyncrasies, and that we loved life; yes, life—all that we saw, everything that was beautiful. Can it be true that our lives are useless, empty, and that we have renounced life out of cowardice? Out of cowardice!

I felt my teeth clench in my mouth and my hands clutch the nickel.

The train kept on crossing fields and more fields, lighting them up for an instant in the light from its cars. I saw the shadow of my body cast on the ground and following me and I said:

"It's true. I must really be a ghost. Everyone, everyone says so."

● ● ●

As we drew near Valladolid my thoughts became a bit calmer. The thorn, oh yes, the thorn was within me, but now I remembered that I had three months before me. It had been three years since I had seen my family and that, for me, was a long time. I had always been somewhat tied to my mother's apron-strings and going home eased all my problems.

Half the family was waiting for me at the station. It's not necessary for me to describe our embraces and kisses when I arrived because I don't think that a priest's are different from those of anyone else.

11

"What about the baby, Crucita?"

"She's at home."

"What's she like?"

"You'll soon see."

With all the hugs I had almost not seen Faustina, the maid who had known me as a child and who now had been with us for many years.

"Faustina, how are you?"

She looked at me, all upset:

"Fine, and you, sir?"

I began to laugh.

"Hey, what's this business of calling me 'sir'?"

"It's just that now you are so . . . different."

Why? Why was Faustina now repeating the words of the English girl? Had everybody agreed to withdraw from me?

My depression lasted only a short time and perhaps it was no more than a passing frown. Then everyone said that I had put on weight, that Rome agreed with me, and that I was very handsome in my cassock. They were seeing me in it for the first time.

• • •

When we reached the house, without waiting for anyone, I ran to my sister's room. There was the baby, asleep in her basket. I couldn't hold back and took her out to devour her with kisses and hugs. The baby complained gently, rubbed her eyes, and then looked at me for a long time without recognizing me; she looked at my cassock and my hat—especially the hat*—and broke out into the most disconsolate crying.

I went to bed sad and thought that I also seemed strange to the baby.

• • •

When I got up in the morning, I was tired and my back hurt all over, for the mattress was too soft and I was used to sleeping on a hard bed. I looked at my room from bed for a few minutes. I went along remembering all the objects one by one and I sighed happily.

The voice of my mother who was playing with the baby came from the kitchen.

"Come on. I'm going to catch you!"

And I jumped out of bed. I put on some slippers, threw my cassock over my pajamas and ran to the kitchen.

I couldn't get the baby to like me. I gave her crackers, candy, I told her that I was going to buy her a ball, that I would take her for a ride on the merry-go-round at the fair, that . . . It was all to no avail. The baby gave me a long look and didn't open her mouth. When I picked her up, she only said "No" and moved back her head so that I couldn't kiss her.

"Kiss your uncle, Is. Don't be silly."

"He's your uncle, Is, and he's come in a log, log twain."

But it was all to no avail.

_____

* Spanish priests wear hats with a low crown and a broad, turned-up brim. R.G.

After Mass I began to look around the house. Things were quite different. Two years before when I had left there had been no children and now that one and a half year old little one invaded everything.

My parents were also very different. I found them younger, more childlike.

Then I went through all the rooms, one by one. I remembered the piano from when I was a boy. I said good morning to the two horrible busts in the dining room and I caressed the backs of my books, lined up on their shelves as they had always been.

Since I did not have much to do, I decided to go out for a stroll around the city. On opening the front door, I came out on a little plaza filled with sun, a round, intimate little plaza where all the superintendents' wives sat in their doorways. I had scarcely taken four steps when one of those limping, shaking buses of our city crossed the square. It was ready to burst. I saw it take the curve— all its timbers creaked as if it were going to come apart— and disappear down María de Molina Street.

I followed the bus around the corner. They had just hosed down the street and it was glistening in the sun. On turning the corner I almost bumped into a group of girls who shouted as they talked. There were four of them who looked like dressmakers and a small girl with a little blue coat.

I heard perfectly:

"Did you notice how young the priest was?"

And then the little girl who shouted:

"Prieeeest!"

14

And the others, laughing:

"Be quiet, silly!"

I didn't know whether to laugh or not. Rather I felt
an uneasiness I do not know how to define. I think it was
then that I fully realized for the first time that I was
wearing a cassock. It got caught between my legs and
kept me from walking. Yes, it was time I made up my
mind: I was enrolled in the class; to people I was a more
or less young priest.

● ● ●

In Zorrilla Square they were building a house and the
workers went up and down the scaffolds. I stood looking
at the house, but I wasn't looking at the building. Rather
I saw those tiny men who seemed to play in the air. What
can they be thinking of me now? Do they hate me? Oh,
if at least they hated me!

I have to confess to this mania of mine. I do not know
if it was born then, but this was the first time I remember
having seriously asked myself, "What do they think of
me?" Since then, when I travel by train or go down the
street, whenever someone stares at me, the question is born
in me: "What do they think of me, that is, of us, of priests?
Oh, if only they hated us! Hating something means really
loving it, considering it important. I don't think anyone
hates ants. Ignorance would hurt me more—a curtain of
silence coming between people, without our being able
to understand each other when we are so near."

From that day on I was pervaded by a feeling of sadness. When I reached the Campo Grande and sat down on a bench, I realized that the entire garden became more serious, that I was a queer bird among the groups of girls who laughed loudly and threw water at each other, and, above all, among the children.

And yet, I felt so close to them . . . And it angered me when some stupid maid said to the children, "Look, if you don't behave yourselves, that man will take you away." I could not know that basically I used to go to the park to watch the children play and that, if I had a book with me, it was so that the "grownups" would not think I was wasting my time.

● ● ●

No, I cannot complain about the children. How can I complain if on leaving the Campo Grande each day there fell on me a gang of fifteen or twenty of them who kissed my hand and covered it with snot? I was not yet a priest, but I didn't say anything to them; they knew no difference between major and minor orders and everyone who wears a cassock was a priest to them. Very gravely, one by one they paraded before me and then hurriedly flew off to continue their interrupted play. I almost felt like crying: there was something special about my hands, something so great that to kiss them was worth interrupting their games and giving up their laughter for a moment. My hands still were nothing, but they, with prodigious intuition, kissed what was going to be.

16

I could not help laughing when the last girl said to the next-to-the-last:

"We gain many indulgences, you know."

THEY ALL CROSSED THE RIVER

LUIS, MY CLASSMATE AND BEST FRIEND, arrived the next morning. A tall, strapping fellow with blond hair—almost always uncombed—and a Germanic face.

He went to say his Mass at the Shrine of the Gran Promesa and, all the way to the church, the only thing I could think was why I could not say Mass as he did instead of having to content myself with serving his. For I had finished my studies and all my friends had sung Mass three months before. Because I was too young, I alone had been left unordained.

And during his Mass it was impossible to avoid thinking. I saw again our entrance into St. Peter's, with rings under our eyes from lack of sleep and a little suitcase in our hands. I saw myself in the sacristy helping them don their vestments, holding them out and almost putting them on for them because they were so wrought up they could barely see; all this while I watched them, full of envy and on the verge of crying.

We entered the basilica which that day seemed more enormous to me than ever. "When we leave they will all be priests except me." And I had to bite my lips. They walked steadily towards the altar, scarcely aware of what they were doing. The Cardinal donned his vestments, Their names, their nineteen names resounded in the basilica. They echoed from wall to wall until they were lost in the heights of the dome. I felt anguish on not hearing my name which somehow had slipped off the list; I alone was left behind on the other shore.

They prostrated themselves and the singing of the litany began. The names of the saints came and went, as if in waves. They—stretched out, dressed in' white like newborn babes—were shouting the great lesson to me: at this instant they were dying, to be reborn different from what they had been. I, who knew them all, who knew their little idiosyncrasies, their pet phrases, everything; I saw them leave my side and swim out into the great sea of God, farther and farther from the shore.

I could not stand witnessing the spectacle. I left the apse and began to wander through the immense naves. From the farthest end of the church, the rise and fall

20

of the litany was heard, just as the tide on a beach. One could feel the saints there; they were coming to call them; they rested a moment over the heads of my friends and withdrew to make way for more and more saints.

People did not cease entering and leaving the basilica. Armed with their guidebooks they snooped around the church, admired Michaelangelo's *Pieta,* the mosaics over the altars, the canopy, the dome. They peered into the apse and asked: "What's going on?" And when I told them: "An ordination," they answered: "Oh," blessed themselves devoutly and went on looking at the tombs of the popes and the jewels of the treasure. And I, I felt like seizing them by the lapel, like shouting to them that what was going on there was something tremendous and that all the art in the world did not matter one bit before the spectacle of nineteen men who were going to become Christ. But no, they wanted to have that cheap culture which they could be conceited about afterwards, something to tell their friends, to seem important a half hour later. Obviously it is more impressive to speak about the Sistine Chapel than of an ordination to the priesthood . . .

The litany ended and I returned to the altar. Now the wonderful moment of miracles was at hand. I wanted to be close to see it and so I asked the man in charge of the candlestick to change places with me. In this way, standing immediately to the right of the Cardinal, I saw all my friends kneeling before the altar.

Then I saw them go up, one by one, holding out

their trembling hands. I saw them place them on the Cardinal's knees; I saw how he made a cross on them with holy oil, and I felt tears come to my eyes.

Julio, Angel, Carlos, Manolo, Antonio, José María . . . all, one after the other. And I thought that those hands which had so often played ping-pong with mine, that wrote poetry, that played the piano, that sketched, were from now on Christ's hands.

And I looked at my own; my poor, sad, sweaty hands that clutched the candlestick until they hurt; I felt the melted wax and tears fall on them.

And they were before me, and yet so distant now.

People continued coming into St. Peter's. They watched it all curiously for a moment and then went off without understanding.

And they were already on the other shore.

And I went on crying, like a child on the beach who sees the ship sail away.

And they were already on the other shore.

And I felt more childlike than ever, smaller, more stupid, more useless.

And they were already on the other shore.

And I knew that they, my friends, my companions, were not much more than I.

But they were already on the other shore.

And I looked about me, thinking that it was a dream, that it had all happened too fast to be true. I looked for something real to grasp hold of, something which would tell me that all that was no more than simply an impressive fiction.

22

But the fact is that they were already far away, seeing me cry from the other shore.

● ● ●

Luis finished his Mass and we went into the city. The street shone in the sun and almost hurt the eyes.

"Luis, it doesn't seem possible."

"Yes, it doesn't seem possible."

We fell silent. We walked a long time without saying a word to each other, as if constrained by the great truth.

"I'm happy. You can't understand how happy I am," he said.

"Yes, I understand."

● ● ●

"Do you know whom I saw the day before yesterday? Gonzalo."

"Gonzalo?"

"Yes, in Barcelona."

Gonzalo! He had not crossed the river either. He had turned back three months before.

When I write these lines, it seems to me that I see him, his eyes brimming with tears and a cigar angrily clenched in his teeth, as we waited for the train to leave. I was deeply moved by his departure because he was a good friend. When, the previous night, biting his lips he told us that he was leaving and asked us to forgive him all the hurt he might have done us, I exploded: "Shut up, stupid!" We looked at each other for a few minutes, knowing full well that there was nothing to forgive and that, perhaps, we were to blame for what was now happening.

We all went to help him pack. There was an imposing silence in his room. All we had to do was say goodbye, but we could not make it short. Perhaps he wanted to be alone and we were bothering him, but it seemed necessary to be there. I remember that José María sat in a corner like a black hulk, without saying a word.

Gonzalo threw his clothes into the suitcases, packing things as they chanced to come into his hands. I remember that a hair shirt came out of the drawer of his nighttable, and, clenching his teeth, he said:

"Who wants 'this'? I certainly don't need it now!"

"No, keep it. Gonzalo, don't be a fool," said Manolo. He took it from his hand and put it in a corner of the suitcase. Gonzalo did not stop him.

"What a fool you are," Manolo said afterward, placing his hand on Gonzalo's head.

Paco and I had not said the rosary that afternoon. We went out to the terrace to say it. There was an enormous moon and the clouds were racing by. It was difficult to pray, difficult and easy. I think I prayed, but not in the phrases of the rosary, because while I mechanically said the Hail Marys, inside I was saying other prayers. Why was Gonzalo leaving? Why had so many others left along the way? I began to think and in a moment had more than forty names. Some had given up when they were still children, simply because it was cold in the seminary or because the food was worse than at home. Others had given up when we were studying Philosophy; they had fallen in love with a pair of blue eyes or a blond head. The smallest number—and the most painful—in the years we studied Theology, perhaps after a brutal struggle with their passions, perhaps because of other, more profound reasons. And Gonzalo, why was he leaving now? Why now, when there were only three months left and he already had all the papers for his ordination? Only God knows. The fact is that he had not crossed the river either.

• • •

Bruno, on the other hand, really crossed it. All the way! He crossed it with such impetus that he left us forever. Bruno reads these lines from heaven.

I remember his tears the day of their ordination, the way he did not know how to cry, his face that was almost funny in spite of his tears, because he wanted to cry hard all at once and it seemed that he cried from his eyes, his nose, and his mouth.

Perhaps no one dreamed of being a priest as he did. He became much more human in those days, less square and mathematical, less casuistic and finical. When he said Mass, Bruno trembled as though he were going to collapse at any minute. And he only said thirty. They brought him to Spain seriously ill with cancer of the stomach and two weeks later we received the news, "Bruno is dead."

Bruno is saying his Masses in Heaven. This joy is left to us. But the gap is open, his room is empty, and his altar without a Mass. Also, death is in our house. The first one has died and someone will be the second. Not even saying Mass frees us from death. But there is one joy: knowing that, on the other side, Bruno will *keep on being* a priest, now and forever, world without end.

BEING A PRIEST WAS . . .

FOR ME, THAT SUMMER WAS FILLED WITH DISCOVERIES, but there is no doubt that discovering the priesthood was the greatest one. It may seem strange, but that is the way it was. How is it possible that, after studying to be a priest for twelve years, I should now discover the priesthood? Well, it's true; the big things are difficult for us to imagine when they are far off. Everything they tell us about them immediately smacks of rhetoric. I had heard, thought and said a thousand times that the priest interceded between God and men, that he was another Christ, and that our function was to bring the world to God, but I think that I had never seriously felt all of this.

Being a priest was to intercede between God and men. That's not very much at all! To intercede, that is, to be chosen by God to speak with men, and chosen by men to communicate with God. To intercede between God and the world, that is to say, to be a man of God and a man of the world, with a good bit of man in him and another good bit of God.

All these things gently pervaded my thoughts until finally they obsessed me. I can assure you that they tormented me and that, when I thought about how enormous the thing was and how small was my reality, I could not help beginning to shake. Men of God! Could it be that we were men of God? Could it be that we had some influence with Him to intercede for men? Could it be that we had some merit, anything, that gave us such a good "in"? Did we at least know how to speak with God? Did we understand God enough to transmit His greatness to men? And, above all, did God matter to men? Were they interested in being united to Him?

When I walked through the streets and saw the men hurrying about their business, their faces hidden behind their newspapers; when I saw them laugh, with a cigarette in their fingers, leaving the movie houses or going into bars and ice cream parlors, I asked myself, "Can it be that they ever think of God?" When I went to twelve o'clock Mass and saw them staring at the ceiling, counting the beams or the rose-windows, I thought, "These are the niggardly minutes they give to God." And I always ended up wondering, "If they care so little about God, what meaning can I have in the lives of these men?" Of course, they did not all think and live this way, but there were so many who did not even realize that they were drifting through life . . .

All this pained me; it pained me even more to think that I was to intercede between men and God. I was—I was going to be—their representative, their deputy. Why, then, did I feel so distant from all of them? Why were my way of seeing life, my worries, the things I talked about, my way of spending my time, so different from theirs? Why was there that barrier of the unknown between us? Why, for example, when they seated me at a table of boys and girls at that party, did I overwhelm them and ruin the dinner for all of us even though I spent the whole time striving to seem congenial to them? Why, when I was in a compartment on the train, did the people, on seeing me, prefer to look for somewhere else to sit, although there were seven empty seats where I was? Their deputy!

Yes. I confess to you that I have suffered greatly because of all this; because this is the truth: we are a race apart. One ought not to dramatize it too much, but it is unquestionable that, beneath the cassock, one is often cut to the heart. It is true that they respect us; sometimes they give us their seat in a streetcar and there are many who love us, but they love us like things that are different, as, for example, a king is loved, and not a friend.

There do not lack people who hate us, who confuse us with the bogey-man—because they say that we ban everything and that we do not let them "live"—who think we are snooty men who take advantage of peoples' faith to live more comfortably; who think that we seek a high position in society; who say . . . But it would be better to leave these things.

Why should it be this way? A hundred thousand times I asked myself this question. I gave myself a hundred thousands answers which were more than enough to convince me. But explanations do not heal the heart. The truth is that I never loved men as I did in those days. Yes, for them and only for them I was becoming a priest. I assure you that it would have been easier for me to become a lawyer, doctor or newspaperman, that perhaps I would have been more *humanly* happy with a wife and children—we will speak of this later—that my life would have perhaps been more enjoyable, because I like the movies and I love bullfights and I do not think I have a vocation to be a recluse. Fine. But man—although he did not know it—needed my help—although he did not ask for it. Man needed my black cassock always to shout to him that God is up there; it was necessary for me to deprive myself of a thousand legitimate pleasures so that they could remember that these pleasures were not the definitive ones. Then let us do everything for man . . . but couldn't he at least understand these things?

I remember that I shouted it to God one day while I was hearing Mass. But I thought at once that love with a reward—and being recognized is enough—is not real devotion because it is fundamentally easy. "It's true," I answered, "but I am a man and I would wish at least . . . "

Being a priest was being another Christ. There was no other sentence that was more monotonously repeated throughout my years of study: *Sacerdos alter Christus*. The priest is another Christ. Priests are Christ on earth.

And the worst thing—and the best—is that this *was* true. It was not an empty phrase; no, it *was* true. The priest usurps the person of Christ; he comes after Him to fill the breach. When he absolves, he does not say, "Christ, through me, forgives your sins," but "I forgive you." And who but God can forgive sins? And at the Consecration of the Mass he does not say, "This is the body of Christ," but "This is My Body."

But such an enormous and consoling thing at the same time made me tremble, because Christ is Christ and we—what are we? Could our hands be compared with the hands of Christ? Can one who has sinned call himself Christ? And I had sinned.

Oh, no. Priests do not kill, they do not steal, they hear Mass every day, they fast when Holy Mother Church bids it, but they are poor children of sin; they can sin and do. I do not speak now to those who delight in inventing slander; I speak only to men of good will. And I am not even discussing the mortal sin in which a priest may some day fall, because he is of the same flesh as the rest; I speak of the idiocy of the little things: meanness, little despicable acts, stinginess, senseless envies, gossip, stupid disloyalties, transgressions against God and against men. I speak of all this, of all these little things which pain God more than the entire string of sins of the world, because we at least know we sin. Yes, there is sin in the world; there are people who drag themselves through the mire of vice, but how have they been formed? What do they know of sin? What do they know of God? They live like animals, brutalized by money, wine or filth and, after all is said and done, one must believe that they don't know what they are doing. But we, yes, we know; they have given us a very thorough education. We have *seen* Love and still we go on with the stupidities that must cut God to the quick.

All this was true. I already knew it that summer and I suffered because of it. We have all suffered and I swear to you that we want to change it, but we are made of flesh and selfishness, and it is not easy to be Christs on earth. If you don't believe it, try it yourself.

I do say one thing to you: that summer I came upon quite a few people who gossiped to me about priests, but not one of those professional charlatans scourged himself for us, and perhaps at the bottom they preferred us to be as we are so that they would have some excuse for the lives they lead.

● ● ●

Being a priest was to love. Yes, to love. I have not made a mistake. Although Nietzsche wrote that "priests are the greatest haters in the world," although we may seem—and perhaps are—gloomy, and though we prune many loves from the tree of our lives, the truth is that being a priest is to love, because love is the essence of Christianity and a priest must be an intensified Christian.

32

I also suffered because of this, because being, as I was to be, a minister of love, I did not know how to love. I want to tell you something that made me think a great deal. This is the way it happened:

It was a fine day. It must have been about five in the afternoon. At that hour it was pleasant in the Park of the East. I liked to sit there in that cool, luminous park with a book in my hand, and I used to go every afternoon. With a book under my arm, I would go as soon as I had dinner, and stay on reading until six. For at six things became complicated: children filled the garden, the swings groaned, and the afternoon was flooded with shouts:

"Come on. It's enough . . . !"

I then continued with my book in my hand and it was almost a pleasure to compare the life in its pages with that other life, so fresh, so spirited.

The day of which I am speaking, my book was going to come off poorly. It was a dismal novel, with many abnormal characters, a good deal of hate, envy and vulgarity, very little sun, and a tremendous emptiness in each soul.

As I turned its pages, I began to rebel: No, no, no, things are not like that. It is not true that life is like that. The sun shines in the world. We have unclouded souls, children, fountains. God exists among men. Man knows how to love, and I love.

And it was true; it was a clear afternoon, a gentle breeze was blowing, and it was delightful to be watching the sun set over the curves of the hoses with which they were watering. What a play of colors! What a magnificent artificial rainbow . . . !

I did not see him come. Perhaps he had been sitting on the bench next to mine for a long time before I noted his presence. I recognized him at once. It was Juan. Yes, Juan the stutterer. And I recalled the scene in my hometown when the owner of the grocery exploded because Juan was taking a half hour to give him a message:

"That's all. Get out of here! I can't have such a numb-skull for a clerk."

I had not seen him again since then. I knew that he had come to the city and that he was the sacristan at Saint Clare's. And now, there he was near me, almost next to me. "It will be better that he doesn't see me," I thought. "I can't bear talking with him."

But the hose was already coming towards his bench.

"Could you, please . . . ," the gardener said to him.

He got up. I saw him come towards me and sit down on my bench. (Shall I say hello to him? If only he doesn't recognize me!)

"G-g-g-good af-afternoon."

"Good afternoon."

Silence. Then he started to talk. (Well, he's recognized me!) There was no way to avoid continuing the dialogue. It was horrible to listen to him. I cut him off quickly as soon as he had said the first word; by guessing what he was going to say, I got ahead of him. But he, unyielding, continued his question.

"Wh-wh-wh-what d-d-do y-you hear fr-fr-from . . . "

"From Castrillo?"

"Y-y-yes, fr-fr-fro-from . . . "

"From Castrillo?"

34

" . . . from C-c-c-c-Castrillo."

I spoke to him at length about the town; I spoke without letup, afraid to see his question come into the void; that frightful stuttering made me nervous. He pointed to my novel and asked me if I was studying. I lied; I told him that I was. I emphasized it and said it quite clearly in order to let him know that he was bothering me. I looked at my watch. I asked him at what time they opened St. Clare's; he told me at five and I showed him my watch, saying:

"It's five now."

"It d-d-doesn't m-m-matter."

He clutched at what I said; perhaps it had been years since he had come across someone from his childhood days. They had been sad days and he had always been the one to pay for the pranks of the rest of us. I saw it in his eyes which shone with joy each time I mentioned a familiar name. I spoke to him furiously, inventing, lying . . . anything to keep him from talking.

It was almost six when he left. As he went off I saw that he was bent over; with the black suit he was wearing he seemed to me a ghost from the world of yesterday. I sighed and felt pity, a terrible pity on seeing his clumsy gait, his tiredness, and, later on, seeing him turn around to say goodbye, as if still wanting to grasp at my hypocritical conversation.

The sun was still shining. The first children came, and men could call life beautiful. I followed him with my eyes to the gate of the garden; I needed to call to him, speak with him, tell him what a brute I had been, walk with him a while and—although it might hurt me; yes, although it might hurt me—let him ask how the harvest was going in the village this year.

And I lacked the courage to do it.

That afternoon, when I stopped in at church, I prayed *very fervently* to God for the first souls He would place in my hands, for the first sinner that I would absolve, for my first Christian, for the first dead man to whom I would open the doors of heaven, for the first boy I would console. And I felt that I was in a church, a bright village church where the people were listening to me as I talked to them of God and of love. (And on doing it, I felt myself a bit of a hero.) And suddenly the church was empty; my bones told me it was empty, and I saw the door open slowly and Juan came in; and he came in heartsick and sad, and he was alone and he prayed to God, stuttering more than ever, because tears fell into his mouth and he could not talk.

I think I cried also that afternoon. I think that I spoke at the top of my voice, that I asked God to free me from being a half-wit and let me live so much in heaven that I would step on my neighbors' feet. I asked Him to engrave on my soul that being a priest was to love, to love without discrimination, to love all the more when it was most difficult, to love all the more when they most needed it, lest it happen that I spend my days intending to be another Christ tomorrow and making my neighbors suffer today.

Yes, I think I cried also that afternoon. For days afterward I returned to the Park of the East with the sole intention of meeting him. But Juan did not return.

Being a priest was having faith. I have always believed that this should be our characteristic virtue: faith, an enormous, unparalleled faith, ready to kneel down before anything which even faintly has to do with God. The priest lives among miracles, he touches them, he works them as if they were the most normal thing in the world, and a great deal of faith is needed to see infinity in such little things.

That summer I began to be very moved by the Mass. I began to understand that we have too much staked in it to remain indifferent.

At the Consecration, when the priest elevated the Host, I would look at my hands and think, "In six months . . . " And slowly, surreptitiously, I put them to my lips and kissed my fingertips. And I asked God with all my heart to make us believe, to make our souls childlike so that we could understand these things, the tremendous plans He had for our hands and for our lips.

I remember that one morning I went to a late Mass— I had returned from a trip the previous night. When almost all the people had left, I witnessed a scene which moved me painfully. There was a priest in the city—he is dead now—a little old priest who had been in an insane asylum and was forbidden to say Mass. I had always felt a special fondness for him that was mixed with pity. That morning he was kneeling in the sanctuary. When there were only two or three of us left in the church, he got up, took the missal from the altar, put three prie-dieux together, and placed the open book on the right-hand one.

He took two steps back and, wearing no vestments,

with only his cassock and without an acolyte, he began his "Mass." I saw him bow down, make the sign of the cross and, one by one, very exactly carry out all the ceremonies. Then he went up to the altar—that is to say, he went to the prie-dieux—kissed the center one and went to the missal to say the Introit, making all the inclinations to the non-existent crucifix.

I could not get over my amazement. I wondered what he would do at the Consecration.

He continued saying his Mass. When he reached the Offertory, he extended his hands and offered a non-existent paten and a non-existent host. Then, acting as though he were taking the cruet, he poured the wine into the chalice and again stretched out his empty hands to heaven.

I was so moved I could scarcely breathe. I realized how dramatic that hollow Mass was.

But he went on. When he reached the Consecration, the two of us were alone in the church. I saw perfectly clearly that his lips moved and that he pronounced the terrible words over—air. *This is My Body,* and then, *This is the chalice of My Blood.* And he slowly raised his hands, as if holding something.

My throat tightened. I saw him believing, reverently bowing down before the air, wanting, *needing* to consecrate Christ and feel the miracle in his hands. There was no way of telling that "that" was not a Mass; he did it all parsimoniously, like something which was completely normal.

And thus the moment for the Communion arrived, and he put his hands to his mouth and moved his teeth as though chewing something; then he lifted the chalice—the chalice of his empty hands—and I saw his throat move, just as if the blood of Christ were flowing through it.

I could wait no longer. I fled from the church as if something terrible had happened to me. No, I cannot explain to you the emotion that I felt; I do not know if it was horror or happiness, if pain or pity. I only know that on leaving the church I could scarcely breathe and that I shouted to Christ, "Lord, may Your miracles never be a pantomime in my hands." And I even wondered if God had not invented some special way—some new trasubstantiation of air—to come to that little priest who raised his empty hands, his lips trembling from faith and miracles.

• • •

Being a priest was being happy. Perhaps not everyone shares this idea with me, but I must tell you that either they do not understand happiness or they do not understand what it is to be a priest.

Nietzsche did not understand it when he wrote that our function was to "enshadow heaven, extinguish the sun, make joy suspicious, devalue hope, paralyze active hands."

No, he did not understand it at all. Being a priest was to have faith in God the Father and hope in the life hereafter. I do not think that these two things are sources of sadness.

As for me, I can tell you that I am a happy man, although perhaps not extremely. Now it is different, but that summer about which I am talking to you, my life was not exactly optimistic. Perhaps it was simply that my clash with life made me fall back; perhaps lack of understanding made me bitter, but the fact is that I spent many hours juggling both nostalgia and bitterness. The world gave me grief, sin hurt me, and I felt alone and powerless and poor. Only with the enormous "booster shots" that God has given me in the past months have I begun to see things as they really are. But we are still going to talk a great, great deal about this.

• • •

And so, among these and many other things I could tell you about, the summer went by and the time came for me to return to the College.

I spent the days before the trip thinking very seriously about what this year was going to mean to me. When I walked through the streets, when I climbed the stairs of my house, when I played the piano, I thought: The next time I come here I will be a priest; a few months from now when I climb these stairs I will climb them as a priest; I will play the piano, and I will play it with the hands of a priest.

The afternoon before I left, I went to the church in which I was to say my first Mass. I sat down on a bench and stayed there a long time without saying a word. I saw myself in my chasuble going up the steps of the altar and elevating the Host; I saw the faithful kneeling before the enormous mystery of my hands; I heard the bell which announced the miracle.

I looked at my hands; I pressed them together; I rubbed at my fingertips in order to clean them; I tried them out for the great moment.

At the station, my mother also kissed them. And when the train pulled away from the platform, I held them out of the window so that they could see them, so that they would learn their exact shape, and seven months later, be able to compare them with my hands of Christ.

GOODBYE TO LIFE

THE ALARM CLOCK STARTLED ME AWAKE at six in the morning. I stretched out in bed. My back ached. I sat up, leaned against the pillows and, one by one, looked at the walls of my room. Yes, they were too white. They would have to be decorated.

I felt tired. It had taken me a long time to fall asleep the previous night. I thought: I'm happy. Why should I have been sad last night? No doubt it was because of the trip, because I was tired. Now I was not saddened by that tiny room, nor by those cold walls, nor by the bed which I would have to make every morning.

I opened the window. The view was not very attractive but I could see a good piece of sky. It was enough for me.

I washed hurriedly and whistled as I went back to the window. "All right, we have to spend the whole year here. Tomorrow I'll count the tiles on the floor. As for the rest, there's precious little to count." Yes, I was definitely happy. Without really knowing why. While I shaved, I grinned at the mirror, as at an old friend: "Hi there, fellow."

On opening the drawer in my night-table, I came across the calendar. June 24th. "We're a little behind the times, aren't we?" And what did that number—268—written in ink under the date mean? Oh, of course. I laughed "The days that are left before the Feast of St. Joseph. I mean, the days that were left. We've made a bit of headway since June." I tore out almost a hundred pages. "Today. October 5," and then I wrote '171'." Yes, today I was definitely happy. I went down to the chapel thinking: "A good number, 171. It even reads the same backwards and forward." And then: "With a 4 in front of it, it's José María's phone number. A good number."

• • •

There was something special about Our Lady of Clemency that always made you smile when you greeted her.

44

She had a sweet face that tried to be a bit Byzantine, but was really a hundred percent Italian. It was easy to love her. And then the name, that sweet, sweet name: Holy Mary of Clemency.

While I was making my meditation, I thought: "Well, boy. In a month you'll be a subdeacon. This is getting serious." And I remembered the words of the ritual for the ordination of subdeacons: "While there is time, reflect. After you have received the order, you will no longer be free to withdraw from the chosen course." Then I had to think about the thing very seriously. I thought about Marisa.

• • •

Marisa . . . I remembered her embroidering at her window, with her two braids falling straight down on her child's breast. I recalled the very day I met her when, a few days after coming from my town after I had finished my second year of philosophy, I was on the balcony leaning on my elbows. The window in the house across the street opened and Marisa looked out, as though she were an apparition. I remember precisely the color of her eyes: a jet black which could only be compared with the black of her hair.

I looked at her. "How pretty she is," I thought. She smiled and withdrew from the window. I wanted to smile also, but I couldn't. I stood there like a fool.

From that afternoon on, I spent most of my time in the room with the balcony, and, sometimes, from my chair,

I would see her embroidering, seated in front of her own window. "It's love," I said to myself. And I used this silly, affected sentence to express it, a sentence that only a child like myself could utter. The only thing I knew about love was what I had read in novels; I had always been tied to my mother's apron-strings and had never been able to think that a girl could be different from a fellow. And it had been just that year when I had discovered two amusingly similar phenomena in my life: the first sprouting of a beard and beginning to think if a girl was pretty or ugly when I passed her on the street. But the truth is that I had never kept looking even for five seconds nor had I felt my heart beat as loudly as now when, seated at the table with a book in my hand, I unceasingly raised my head to see if she appeared.

A few days later I felt her near. It was at the running of the young bulls. Since all the fields that surrounded the town could be seen from the church tower, it was a privileged place from which to watch the folding of the bulls. The whole swarm of us altar boys and seminarians used to gather with the parish priest under "Nicolasa," the enormous bell. It was then—why?—that Marisa came. I felt the entire morning grow brighter. And when the priest told us, "Make room for these girls," I realized that I was pressing against the wall and that my eyes were pointing out to her a place next to me.

We were all very tightly pressed together and, when the bulls appeared on the horizon, sixteen hands pointed them out from the belfry. The bell-ringer shouted, "Cover your ears," and pulled the clapper. It seemed as if the whole tower were shaking and we looked fearfully towards the bronze bell and, pressing our fingers against our ears, all laughed together. Marisa was in front of me and laughed without letup (she laughed with her whole body); I did not know what was happening to me. The folding didn't matter one bit to me any more. "Lord, how pretty she is, how pretty she is!" And I thought, "Eighteen. She must be eighteen years old."

And her braids . . . I was obsessed by the one which fell over my right shoulder. To touch it, oh, if only I could caress that braid! And I was moving my shaking hand towards it when the bell began to ring again and she suddenly turned around, laughing and shouting.

The bulls passed below the bell tower and only at that instant did I stop looking at her. Then we went down. I wanted to speak to her.

"Do you want to come to my balcony? You can see better there."

"No, I can't. I'm going with my friends."

Now she was looking at me. Then she said to me:

"The other day I saw you serving Mass. You were very . . ."

I felt myself blush. And I said to her.

"Marisa."

But she was already running after her friends.

We didn't have to agree that the best time to see each other was during the siesta. Without fail, every day at the same hour, she sat at her window with her embroidery and I on my balcony with a book. We scarcely ever spoke; we only looked at each other and smiled. Just once, when the summer was drawing to an end and it was time for me to return to the seminary, did she sadly say to me:

"Don't forget me."

And I, very seriously:

"I won't forget you."

It is odd that until I was back in the seminary I did not realize that all this childishness was not very much in keeping with my dreams of being a priest. I did feel a strange fear, but love of the unknown made me overcome it.

Once in the seminary I began to laugh at myself and, while I did not forget Marisa, all that began to be something distant and funny to me and I think that I would have forgotten her completely had I not seen her again.

The following summer I was really afraid when I took the train to my town. I remember that on leaving the chapel, trembling with emotion, I said to Our Lady, "Let me come back, Mother, let me come back." And I left the seminary as though I were never to return.

On approaching the town, I promised not to see Marisa, but such a momentous promise necessarily had to end up by my seeing her. And I did. But in that first instant I understood that everything had changed. She had cut her braids and was obviously a girl on her way to becoming a woman; and in my eyes there was no longer the innocent surprise of a year earlier. Now I understood that it was not right and that that was not the road to the priesthood.

And I went off, angry with myself. In church that afternoon I angrily bit my fingers as I knelt in the pew. And that rage did its job. From time to time I would see her again, but I knew that I would again become angry with myself in the afternoon and that this anger was going to take me from the balcony first for a week, then ten days and then two weeks. The day I took the train to go to Rome for the first time, I did not say goodbye to her and I mailed a letter from the station in Burgos: "Marisa, you must forgive me. I had to decide and I have. I could not keep on playing that way."

As soon as we reached Rome we began our Spiritual Exercises. It was a week that I devoted in its entirety to thinking about the problem of my vocation. I explained it all to the director of the Exercises and when they were over I wrote a letter of which I keep a copy.

Marisa: I think that I need to write to you, that it is necessary for us to speak at least once, no matter how painful it is for us. Ten days ago you probably received a few lines from me which made you suffer. Now I think they were too brusque. Forgive me. I assure you that I am sorry, because the truth is this: I still love you. No, don't misinterpret these words; I have not changed my mind. Our affair is completely over; you must not get your hopes up. But I want you to know that if it has ended it is not because I have lost all affection for you. It is because I have realized that there is a greater love in my soul.

I don't know if you understand, Marisa. I realize full well that it is difficult to understand. Perhaps even I do not understand it wholly. Look, I have thought a great deal about it in these past days. I have thought it out and have weighed everything carefully, sensibly, and with a serenity that almost amazes me. You must understand. It was not a question of loving you or not. It was a question of giving myself entirely to you or to the Other One. It was not the struggle of your love with my comfort or my career. It was the struggle between your love and another Love. The greater of the two has conquered. Forgive me, my darling, but this is what has happened.

It makes me suffer to think that I have perhaps hurt you, that I have given you hopes which today I must cruelly destroy. But you have to understand this mistake of mine. I also am but a child, or rather, I have been one until now. I have dreamed of you and I assure you that it has not been easy for me to uproot this dream. You ask me what can be worth such a great sacrifice. In order to answer you, I would have to speak to you of the priesthood and of Christ with words that even I do not yet understand, but—I haven't the least doubt—I know that I will understand one day soon. And you will understand too. Marisa, you must see.

I should not like you to cry when you read this letter. Remember that I love you, that I still love you, in a different but also in a much purer way. Perhaps you are thinking that I am very calm, that I am even tranquil enough to make pretty phrases when I say goodbye. You are wrong if you think it. Once again it's an inner thing.

And now I am going to begin my greatest sacrifice. My spiritual director has told me: "Try to forget her. But I want you to know that you never will, not completely. That's why you must get used to seeing her not as a

50

temptation but as a sister. When her image comes to mind, think that you are a priest and that you are going to give her Communion."

Maybe this advice seems strange to you, but he is very old and this is the way he said it. After the brief experience of these past days, I can assure you that when I follow his advice I feel an inexplicable sensation of tenderness that has absolutely nothing to do with sin.

I must tell you goodbye. This is going to be the last letter that I write you. I would also prefer you not to answer. Why keep on with something that can go no further?

Try to forget me and don't suffer uselessly. I know you will find the man who will make you happy because this is what you deserve and I am constantly going to ask God to grant it to you. Look, we have to believe in Him, for He is the One who is tearing me from your hands; but if this is what He does, it is because it is best for us both, although we may suffer and not understand. You'll see how one day we will both be proud of this decision.

Pray for me, Marisa. Pray to God that I forget you. For my sake make this supreme sacrifice of praying that I forget you. Show me your love in this way. I am going to do the same in order that you forget me.

I don't know what to say so as to avoid ending on a tone of tragedy. I will tell you simply: Goodbye, Marisa.

● ● ●

This was, so to speak, my "initiation in love." Backwardness in knowing life, fear on reaching the moment of becoming a man, a short love story, and, suddenly, beginning to think seriously about things.

Passion wasn't long in making its appearance. There came the obsessive dreams; the flesh, without need for dreams; rubbing my eyes with my fists; temptation without rhetoric; more or less brutal desires, and manhood. There came disgust with everything, sadness, a closing-up of my heart, a tragic sense in my understanding of life; church became the greatest torture of all, and going to Communion savored of nothing. I thought my cassock weighed upon me and many times I said to myself, "This is going to pieces."

I don't know if the same thing was happening to my companions. Perhaps they all went through it before or afterwards, because life is basically the same for everyone and he who has lived one life fully can say that he has lived all lives. Yes, we have felt almost everything that you have felt, because it is not the streets that make life, but one's own soul. And this has been perhaps more painful in all of us than in the rest for it has always played at cross purposes with that other world of ideals and of hoping for such enormous things. Yes, temptation is hard but, when you know where you are going, the knowledge of your own idiocy hurts even more. The most painful thing is not loving the flesh nor even feeling that you love it; the tremendous part is knowing that you are going to be a priest, that you want it with every fiber in your soul, and that our lowest part—but, after all is said and done, ours—does not leave off loving and desiring the flesh.

I believe we have all felt that moment of desperation and rage. That pain of seeing that our lives—which should be a pure line of light—bob up and down like a cork in the sea. It is feeling that in the morning you promise God to save the world and at noon can't take your eye off a girl who is passing by—and, at the same time, still wanting to save the world. Being holy is very difficult. Perhaps wanting to be is enough. But the great difficulty does not lie in being holy; rather it is in becoming holy, along all that hollow road of emptiness, always playing hide-and-seek with God and the devil. Oh, how our stinginess at surrendering ourselves hurts!

● ● ●

I still have not spoken to you of loneliness nor of children. They usually talk too much about the pleasure, about the flesh which priests renounce, as if celibacy were only renouncing carnal pleasure. This is too naïve an idea. Perhaps the most truly painful aspect of renunciation is much more human and much deeper; it is loneliness.

It has always been terrifying for me to go to cemeteries and see that the only graves that no one visits, the only ones without flowers are . . . ours. We give ourselves to all men to such an extent that no one feels it is his concern when he sees our forsaken graves. No, we know that there is nothing to be gained by having flowers on our graves, but one always dreams that someone will mourn us when we are gone. And who loves an old priest? When their mothers or their sisters die and the house begins to fill with dust and their cassocks to have holes in them, priests ought to remember their ordination as subdeacons. Yes, they also dreamed of a warm house, supper ready on the table, some children to kiss, a pair of warm slippers on getting up in the morning.

When I am an old man and come indoors blowing on my hands after four hours of hearing confessions, what will my house be like? I know that I will not be able to open the door and shout: "Marisa!" and hear a little girl's steps—because our daughter will be named after her—nor be smothered with kisses. Nor will she come later with her great black eyes and see from afar that our daughter loves me. I know we will not sit down to the table together and Antonio will not come—he is in his second year of medical school now—nor Marianín who is half way through the Institute. I will be alone, eating a dish of miserably cooked beans, angrily biting at my bread and I will be able to tell no one of my sadness; it will stay within me and make me bitter. Then they will say that I have a bad temper and even my assistants will think that my mind is beginning to weaken.

But come, Marisa. Why don't you come? The house is so lonely. . . Couldn't you come to put some flowers on my windowsill? I am a poor old man. How do you expect me to know when to water the flowers and when they have to be taken out on the balcony? My books are covered with dust. Yes, Felisa. . . You know that Felisa has never been very clean. Besides, she is old. We are two poor old people in a big house older than ourselves. Could not one

54

of our children come and laugh? Someone has to laugh in this house. Laughter is like varnish on the furniture. And here no one has laughed for years.

I am going to feel lonely this afternoon, Marisa. Like so many other afternoons. We were children then. I gave you up with the clearest of consciences. No, I don't regret it now. I knew perfectly well that this was going to happen. Yes, yes, I knew loneliness. I complain simply for the sake of complaining, but this, I knew perfectly well that it was going to happen. Yes, Marisa, I know that you do not understand the reason for this sacrifice. Very few people do. Not even I understand it fully. BUT GOD DOES.

● ● ●

I recalled all this now, but not with an air of sadness. They were like things that had nothing to do with me; they seemed to be someone else's story. Marisa was in that vague region of fiction or of half remembered dreams. For, after the suffering and after that romantic period in my life, peace had come little by little. My prayer more and more had come to resemble a conversation between lovers, and love for God, which a few years before had been so difficult for me, now seemed more and more real and, I would even say, more like my love for Marisa, but without that trembling of the heart.

When the time for it arrived, this renunciation was not the tearing myself away of four years before, but rather something very simple, very elementary—no more than merely giving myself over.

One of those afternoons—ten or twelve days before the ordination—Alfredo read me his poem "On the Eve of Being Ordained Subdeacon." Alfredo was the oldest one in our class. He had been a doctor and now he dreamed of the priesthood with the same anticipation as the rest of us. I knew that he wrote poetry, but I never thought he was so good. Therefore, while he was reading his poem and I felt my heart jump at the sound of the verses, I could not contain my surprise. In the poem he told how that night—precisely the night before his ordination as subdeacon—he had felt his flesh shaken by all the cries of his children who were calling him from the void.

> And I whispered their names.
> One is called Alfredo, like me.
> His curly hair
> vanished
> among the stars.
> What an uproar in his hands
> when I brought him the big red dog
> I saw yesterday afternoon
> in the toystore on the corner!
> I named another Federico;
> like my father,
> like my grandfather.
> And a little daughter with dancing eyes
> in the void
> now bears my mother's name.

Yes, there were our children, there, with their flesh and their names. There, dreaming of their toys. Our children who would never be born.

> I saw them, Lord!
> I touched in the night
> their weeping heads,
> the heads tortured
> by the brutal anxiety
> of being.
> Nothingness is a terrible ill.
> Frenetically they moved, and moved again
> their hands, their shadowy hands,
> wanting to touch their aching bodies
> and they could not find them.
> Their throats—which never knew
> the miracle of a sip of cool water—
> cried to me feverishly
> with red shouts
> because now they would always be
> nothing. (1)

The poem stirred the very fibers of my heart. Children, yes, one speaks little of them. And yet they are what hurt most at the hour of taking the great step. I, who have always loved children madly, what wouldn't I give to have a son, to feel in my hands a bit of my own flesh? And I recalled the summer afternoon that I took a nap

---

(1) This poem was published in its entirety in Number 5 of *Estría, Cuadernos de poesía del Colegio Español de Roma.*

and Crucita's baby lay at my side. There, that little body, scarcely a year old, seeing her tiny chest rise and fall, with her blond, curly hair shining on the white pillow. . .

I did not sleep that afternoon. I began to fondle her gently and I felt that I was on the verge of crying. I would have given my life to know that she was my daughter.

I confess to you that I have suffered greatly because of this. When I see my brother and sister playing with their children, when I see that the children are the center of their lives, when I see my house happy and overflowing with love, I cannot help thinking of certain things. Yes, one had to give up all this—and forever.

●　●　●

I have told you all this so as not to sound my own trumpet too loudly and make you think that I am a hero and all that. I tell it to you because there are people who think we are cowards and have no feelings. No; I assure you that priests are not men who have been failures in life; we are not poor souls born with our eyes shut tight. I, at least, am not; I'm very sure of it. It would have been easy for me to build a home and even live in it with relative comfort. My brother and sister have done it. The flesh? Yes, it attracts me. Children? Yes, they hurt me; I am not lacking in affection. For a greater love have I closed my doors on the world. When one is twenty-three he knows pretty well what world he lives in.

58

And why does one become a priest? What is there, what can there be that merits and demands all these renunciations? Does one become a priest in order to live more comfortably? To have an elegant place in society? To have heaven guaranteed? Not to work?

I cannot tell you why all my classmates were becoming priests. I can only say that I became a priest for you, to hold out my hand to men, perhaps to be the thorn in your lives that makes you remember always that there is a God above us and that there is a blood He shed for us.

I remember Delanoy's movie—as controversial as it was magnificent—called *God Needs Men*. We argued quite a bit about the title *Men Need God* being perhaps more exact and finally agreed that the phrase which would include the whole idea of the picture would be "God needs men to help Him save the men who need God."

Yes, that's what it is. That is the priesthood. For two thousand years that trumpet has blown, that marvelous need for God. Oh, our God without hands, our handcuffed God who needs us as crutches to reach the rest of humanity! Oh, the world of souls, as hard and dry as the earth of Castile, and we, my hands, like channels through which God comes, through which God wants to come; God, like an immense blind man who comes to give us light, but who needs a hand to help him cross the street.

Yes, this is what it means, this marvelous thing of lending God our eyes and hands, our feet and words so that He can come to us.

When I thought of all this, it seemed so ridiculous to me to think of renunciation. Renouncing what? What, my God? Renouncing fatherhood! I laughed. Why now I feel that I am a father in the full sense of this wonderful word! And I remembered Alfred's poem, and I said with him that my destiny is

> To take hold of the
> ordinary, everyday people
> who pass at my side
> counting out their change
> for the trivial streetcar ticket,
> chewing gum
> and reading newspapers,
> forgetting You and themselves,
> being only vague figures
> in Your scheme of men;
> to take hold of them and say
> that they must yet be born anew
> if they will be Men as You ordain.
> And to think that it is I who am to beget them
> complete men!
> And so, afterwards, when in their fingers
> the rose of Your Grace
> is in full flower
> and their hearts
> tinkle within like dew-covered bells,
> there will be the fresh sound in my ears
> of the longed-for, happy song
> they will sing to call me:
>   Father . . . Father . . . Father . . . "

60

Lord.
I am going to people Your Heaven
with these children of my hands,
my baptizing, forgiving,
giving Bread hands.
And thus, Your enormous House
will be filled with the children
of my children, and the grandchildren of my
grandchildren.

• • •

Now I want to tell you this: I was happy. In spite of
everything, I was happy. There is usually a funereal air
about the subdiaconate. It is true that renunciation is
hard, but I did not have the impression of losing anything
or of being left maimed; rather, quite to the contrary, I
was going to be more complete than ever. No, I didn't
feel that I was a hero when I gave God my chastity. Perhaps I felt more like a profiteer who was putting in two
and taking out ten.

I remember that the night before the Feast of Christ
the King, while the logical thing would have been to think
of how decisive was the step I was about to take the following day, I went up to the terrace—the sky was aflame
with stars—and began to whistle like a little boy. I had
a heart to heart talk with God; I wanted to sing and
jump. I had an undefinable inner joy, as if playful water
were flowing through my veins instead of blood. We were

going to take a decisive step; we were walking into the void, but it was a familiar void—the void of God—and there one could stand on his head without having even to think about it.

That afternoon when they gave us the vestments in the sacristy for the next day, I said, "This is really serious now." And on saying it I felt inexpressible joy.

● ● ●

With the white albs reaching our feet—angelic garments which speak to us of purity—we entered the baroque church in a procession. Not a very popular church, it was quite scantily decorated. Beautiful, yes, but it gave me the impression of being a dance hall. There was a vaulted ceiling which shone with gold and a great nave mirrored in marble. But that day I felt extraordinarily happy. I knew the importance of the moment and, when I realized that I was entering the sanctuary, I thought that the marble balustrade which separated me from the eighty or a hundred people in the church was like a wide river we were crossing and that through it we were entering the seas of God and moving away from the world.

Physically, the Bishop wasn't much to look at. Short and thin, he peered out from behind gold-rimmed glasses and his look was deep and inquisitive, but underlying it was a smile that he seemed to be holding in reserve. He conducted the ceremonies naturally, like one who has done it many times before, but not as though it were just routine for him; and his Latin did not sound like a sleepy psalmody but rather something alive that made sense.

The minor orders came first, and I remembered mine of the previous year. My tonsure in Propaganda Fide Church, when, surrounded by Negroes and Chinese, I was inducted into the army of God; and the four minor orders which were conferred two by two in the College chapel, like so many stairs which brought me to the threshold I was now going to cross.

When a fat, bald monsignor called us in his shrill voice: *Let those who are to be ordained subdeacons come forward* and afterwards named us one by one, I remember the joy with which I gave my *Adsum. I am here.* What seemed merely a weathered, routine formula was for me a dream that I had cherished for thirteen years. It was Christ's official call, through the Bishop, to be His minister; it was His definitive invitation to a state I could still accept or refuse.

Now, indeed, I could see that I had a vocation to the priesthood. In that instant I remembered my childhood years when, for the first time, I wanted to go to the seminary, but without concretely knowing why; perhaps only because the seminary had large playgrounds and for Christmas they put on plays that made you split your sides with laughter. I remembered the years I studied Philosophy, in which priests seemed heroes out of fairy tales, and my first years of Theology when we were torn from life and exiled from the present. And here I was, perfectly calm now, feeling the priesthood as it really was, without

63

tremendous words but with all the immensity of its greatness.

We lined up before the Bishop who spoke to us:

"Dearly beloved sons, you are about to be promoted to the sacred order of subdeaconship. Again and again you must carefully consider the office for which you ask today of your own accord. For as yet you are free: if you so decide, you may pass over lawfully to secular pursuits; but after you have received this order, you will be free no longer to withdraw from the chosen course, but bound for life to the service of God, whom to serve is to rule. And you will be under obligation, with His help, to observe chastity and to employ yourselves in the ministry of the Church at all times. Therefore, while there is time, reflect. If you decide to persevere in your holy resolve, come forward in the name of the Lord."

The Bishop pronounced these words as solemnly as befitted their meaning and we listened to them with the same solemnity. Like fourteen automatons we took a step forward. All was fulfilled; the river was crossed and liberty ended; we had cleared the abyss of God. Now the world sounded far distant; the noises of the cars which were beginning to make their morning journey across the city and whose motors made the church windows shake seemed to come from another planet. All was behind us now. The door was open. And a hundred feet away—a hundred days—was the priesthood.

Marisa, I assure you that you did not hurt me then. Forgive me. I saw you as a girl, as you were when I knew you, with your dark braids falling down your back;

I smiled at you as I might to my sister; I saw you later dressed in white in a church filled with lilies while I placed your hand in that of the man who is going to make you happy; and, looking at me, you wept on understanding how well God has done all things; and I saw your house, I saw your children running about the room—at Epiphany will you let me put a toy at my window for them? —and I saw you teaching them the Hail Mary; and, all dressed in white, taking them by the hand to a prie-dieu to which I will come with the white bread in my hand.

You, now, do not know that I have taken this step, but no doubt it has snowed in the village and you have gone to the window and you will see my balcony covered with snow, as white as my alb. I know that you are not sad today. You have forgotten my name a little because there is another that covers it. And you smile.

$$\bullet \quad \bullet \quad \bullet$$

Now the fourteen of us are prostrated along with those who are to be ordained deacons and priests. It has also snowed on the sanctuary, for it is covered with forty bodies clothed in white. There we are like dead men or new-born babes, buried with Christ and ready to be born anew.

The choir has begun to chant the Litany and suddenly the church fills with mystery. All the saints answer to the invocation and there is a fluttering of wings all through the vaults of the church. We feel them, like giant waves which pass over our heads.

Holy Mary—and She comes, lily-white (She holds my
  mother by the hand)—.
St. Michael—the defense of our back is here now; he
  girds on our armor—.
St. Gabriel—the annunciation of our priesthood now:
  Blessed will be your hands among all hands—.
St. Peter—oh, you, firmness of most solid stone!—.
St. Paul—with the vibrant sword of his living word—.
St. Stephen, St. Lawrence, St. Vincent, St. Gregory,
  St. Benedict, St. Francis, St. Agnes, St. Cecilia:
all the saints, all of them came and went above our heads.
God Himself was there beside us; His weight could be felt
on our backs; one had only to lift his head to see Him. And
now it was happiness that coursed through our veins like
a joyful flash of lightning because, finally, the door was
open and we had only to stretch out our hands.

While all we subdeacons knelt before the altar, the
Bishop explained to us that our office was in the proxi-
mity of the altar; our duty was to prepare the water and
wine for the sacrifice of the Mass, to receive the offerings
and hand the celebrant the bread for the Mass.

The offices of deacon and subdeacon had true signi-
ficance in the early centuries of the Church when they
were genuine assistants of the priest in his ministry and
apostolate. Today, the two orders merely signify steps towards the priesthood, steps of varying degrees of surrender
to and reception of Christ. It is because of this that everything in these ceremonies has a mystical, symbolic meaning
and, for the ordinands, they are two bugle calls to attention
before the reality which is drawing near. The ritual reads:

If *hitherto you have been tardy as to the church, hence-forth you must be prompt. If hitherto you have been prone to indulge in sleep, henceforth you must be vigilant. If hitherto you have been given to drink, henceforth you must be temperate. If hitherto you have been wanting in honor, henceforth you must be without reproach. May He deign to grant it to you, who lives and reigns, God, forever and ever.*

Then we all arose and, kneeling two by two before the Bishop with our hands on the Chalice and the paten, heard him say:

Behold what ministry is entrusted to you. There-fore, I exhort you so to conduct yourselves as to be pleasing to God.

And after saying two prayers that asked God to make us *valiant and watchful sentinels of the heavenly army* and entreated Him to make the gifts of the Holy Spirit descend upon us, the Bishop invested us one by one with the insignia of the subdiaconate.

Receive the amice, by which is signified moderation of speech.

And he pulled it over our heads.

Receive the maniple, by which are signified the fruits of good works.

And he tied it to our arm.

May the Lord clothe thee with the tunic of gladness and the garment of joy.

And all our body felt cloaked in the armor of God. And after placing our hands on the book of the Epistles, we returned to our places, our eyes radiant with joy.

Lord, why is it that, precisely at this moment which might well seem painful, you clothe us in "the tunic of gladness and the garment of joy?" It is usually said that the priesthood and the diaconate are times for receiving and the subdiaconate time to give—and it is always hard to give. But I can assure you that I made no tragedy out of my renunciation. Indeed, we do give and, in human terms, it might seem that we give a lot; but was it not ridiculous to crow over it when, on giving it to God, He was already letting us see close-up all that He was going to give us a few short days later?

I was very happy, I tell you. No longer was there any possible choice, no possible freedom; but, when I left the church while the whole city tore through the streets, I felt freer and more complete than ever, as if rid of a tiresome burden.

RECEIVE THE HOLY SPIRIT

THE TRUTH IS THAT MY ORDINATION TO THE DIACONATE SCARCELY IMPRESSED ME. Much more important than what it was, was the promise it held. Of course I realized how magnificent it is to receive the Holy Spirit, but the priesthood was so near that everything savored of my next ordination. Thus, when I prostrated myself during the Litany, I thought, "Just once more." And when the Bishop imposed his hands on my head, I said, "The next time he does it . . . " I understand that it should not have been this way, but this way it was.

Perhaps I was not up to par that day, perhaps it was that the atmosphere of the great basilica—it was conferred in St. John Lateran—did not lend itself to recollection. (Still, I am happy to have been ordained there, because St. John Lateran is the mother and head of all the churches of the world; today, on remembering it, I think that my ordination as deacon is the symbol of my union with the Universal Church and of my Catholicism.)

Of course, one mustn't exaggerate either. It is not true that I was unmoved when I felt the Holy Spirit pervading my soul like a sea, filling every nook and cranny; but, for me, it was all like the day before a holiday. Moreover, it was Christmas day and, on that day, I have never been able to take things seriously.

Thus it did not surprise me that at dinner no one spoke of our ordination as deacons, but rather of the year that was soon to begin and which was going to be the most important year in our lives.

It was then that Antonio went up to the pulpit in the dining room and read us a wonderful proclamation which amazed all of us because no one had known he wrote so well. (I think it was the Holy Spirit who wanted to show us that he can inspire, in spite of the fact that we had not paid very much attention to Him in the morning.) The proclamation was wonderful because it moderated things; it combined happiness with spirituality, and high jinks with Grace. I think we all felt better after hearing it. This is the way it read:

Unto you we announce great joy:
the Son of God has been born to us in 120 cribs.

Unto you we announce deep peace:
the peace of twenty boys who are very soon to be altars.

Unto you we announce very great happiness!
Then rejoice, as almond trees when they feel they are
trunks of purity.

Rejoice, as straw when it feels it is the mattress of God.

Rejoice, as hearts when they feel they are a mother's
breast.

Rejoice, as hands when they feel they are sunlit mountains.
Do you know what the King says?
Unto us there will today be born a Child,
and tomorrow will be born a Mass.
This is the Christmas that repeats the crib
and announces a host.

Rejoice! Rejoice! Rejoice!

And it will come to pass that:
There will be marzipan. Glory to God in the highest.

But self-denial will go on. More glory to God in the
highest.

There will be tournaments. Glory to God in the highest.

But there will be more calls to grace. More glory to God
in the highest.

There will be movies. Glory to God in the highest.

But there will also be super-invitations to recollection.
More glory to God in the highest.

There will be closed books. Glory to God in the highest.
But there will be open stables. More glory to God in the highest.
Today, the 24th, we make this proclamation, Adeste. (1)
Later we will begin the holiday in the refectory. Fideles.
There will be decorating of Common-rooms and applause in the martyrology. Laeti.
And solemn high Mass. Triumfantes.
You already know the official schedule. Venite.
You already know the days for retreat and the hours of prayer. Adoremus.
And the first of January of the year dedicated to our priesthood will be our joy. Dominum.
This is what the King says. We repeat it to you:
Christmas, 1952 has come.
What it means:
The Christmas before our priesthood has come.
Remember to give your hearts to the Child and play ping-pong.
Give way to uproarious joy,
    but knowing that it is not He.
Remember the marzipan in the kitchen,
    but also the children in the huts.
Listen to the radio,
but do not fail, even for a moment, to listen to your hearts.
And above all remember the 19th of March.
Know that this year we are pure expectation;
join the crib and the altar, for they are good friends,
and say many times when you swallow your chicken:

---

(1) This is a paraphrase of the Christmas versicle: *"Adeste-fideles-laeti-triumfantes.
    —Venite-adoremus-dominum."* "Oh come, all ye faithful, joyful and tri-
    umphant.—Come, let us adore the Lord."

Glory to God in the highest.
Rejoice! Rejoice! Rejoice!
Unto us is born a Child
and this time the Virgin will put Him in our hands.

This is how our Christmas began, that wonderful kind of Christmas you can spend in a seminary (although a bit homesick) when the air is filled with true family love and warmth. And again we saw the superiors dancing in circles and playing the tambourine; and there were all sorts of pranks on the Feast of the Holy Innocents*; and we argued about the movies; and we sang carols to a Child who had a damaged hand and a St. Joseph with the funniest naive face.

Christmas Eve is coming,
Christmas Eve is going,
and we will go away
and—ay!—we won't come back again.

* The Spanish equivalent of April Fool's Day. R.G.

NINETEEN HUNDRED AND FIFTY-THREE

DECEMBER 31, 1952—THIS AFTERNOON IN THE RE-
TREAT I decided to keep a diary during these first months
of the year of my priesthood. It's not that I set much store
by diaries because I know from experience how stupid
they are. But at any rate it's amusing for me to pick up
the pages I scribbled during my first years of Philosophy.

I think also that these three months are something
special in my life and that in a few years there will be
many moments in which clutching at them will be my
one recourse.

I cannot scorn sentiment for fear of sentimentality, and I think that everything I store up in my heart in these months is headway for the empty days to come.

JANUARY 1—A great day. Today we have celebrated the holiday of *our* year. 1953. I have to really learn this number.

The affair consisted in the following: after dinner we set up the counter. In the Common-room (1) we have placed a large green board and on it two red numbers almost a foot and a half high. 77. That's how many days are left before the Feast of St. Joseph. Each day the numbers will go down and our fear will gradually increase as the numbers on the board decrease.

The best part of the day was after the siesta when we met in the chapel. We wanted to "preview" or "prelive" the ordination ceremony and so, although quite a bit abridged, we followed the Ritual.

The 24 of us who are to be ordained this year of 1953 (on St. Joseph's or other days) knelt before the altar at which we will be ordained. The Rector went up to the chancel and from there, as though he were the bishop, read us the prayer *Consecrandi filii carissimi* which is like the beginning of the ordination. In it he exhorted us to think about the meaning of the priesthood and the tremendous dignity it brings to us.

Afterwards came the Litany. But it was a very odd one.

After the usual opening invocations, as in the Ritual,

---

(1) The Common-room is the meeting place of each class, decorated by us according to our tastes (tastes which, by the way, are not exactly old-fashioned).

each one made a petition, *his* petition on the eve of becoming a priest. None of us knew those of the rest and it was very moving. Each one read his—and it was wonderful to see all his character and soul mirrored in it; each one read his petition in his normal voice, but we all trembled a bit. There was a terrible silence in the chapel, for we were alone, and we had all bared our souls.

Later we gathered up the petitions and the litany turns out to be very beautiful, especially because you see in it what 24 boys ask God just before their ordination to the priesthood. Of course the best part of the litany is seeing each person reflected in his petition and only we know this.

Lord, have mercy on us.
Christ, have mercy on us.
Lord, have mercy on us.
Christ, hear us.
Christ, graciously hear us.
God the Father of heaven, have mercy on us.
God the Son, Redeemer of the world, have mercy on us.
God the Holy Spirit, have mercy on us.
Holy Trinity, one God, have mercy on us.
Holy Mary, pray for us.
All you holy Saints of heaven, pray for us.
We sinners, We beseech You, hear us.
That You would vouchsafe to bless these elect, We beseech
    You, hear us.

That You would vouchsafe to bless and sanctify these elect, We beseech You, hear us.

That You would vouchsafe to bless, sanctify and consecrate these elect, We beseech You, hear us.

Thus far the Ritual. Then we began our own petitions, reading them one by one, with the others responding.

That You would vouchsafe to make us carry out with evangelic spirit all the dreamed of anxieties of our priesthood, We beseech You, hear us.

That You would vouchsafe to make our priesthood truly missionary, a testimony of our Roman Catholicism, We beseech You, hear us.

That You would vouchsafe to make the Spirit of faith increase in us, We beseech You, hear us.

That You would vouchsafe to make the Our Father the concrete norm of our behavior in life, We beseech You, hear us.

That You would vouchsafe to make us 24 humble priests, We beseech You, hear us.

That You would vouchsafe to make the *Ad Deum qui laetificat iuventutum meam* (2) of our last Mass as true as in our first, We beseech You, hear us.

That You would vouchsafe to let us not collect commissions from You, We beseech You, hear us.

That You would vouchsafe to make us want to be friends to seminarians and help them when we are priests, We beseech You, hear us.

---

(2) "I will go unto the altar of God, unto God, who giveth joy to my youth." (From the prayers at the foot of the altar.)

That You would vouchsafe to let us face reality, but always remember that You are the first reality, We beseech You, hear us.

That You would vouchsafe to aid us to use our time well for the greater glory of God and the salvation of souls, We beseech You, hear us.

That You would vouchsafe to make us think in a Catholic and universal way, We beseech You, hear us.

That You would vouchsafe to make us feel Your divine Providence in all things, We beseech You, hear us.

That You would vouchsafe to let us want no other joy but that of living united to You, We beseech You, hear us.

That You would vouchsafe to let us always be reminded of our misery and never think ourselves anything without You, We beseech You, hear us.

That You would vouchsafe to let our lives be a YES in answer to Christ, We beseech You, hear us.

That You would vouchsafe to never let us say NO to You, We beseech You, hear us. (3)

That You would vouchsafe to let us do Your most holy will at all times, We beseech You, hear us.

That You would vouchsafe to grant us the optimism of a complete surrender without complexes of tragedy, We beseech You, hear us.

That You would vouchsafe to let us never hinder Your action in souls, We beseech You, hear us.

That You would vouchsafe to let us not find strange the miracles we will have in our hands and never doubt

---

(3) I copy these petitions (the one with the "yes" and the one with the "no") one after the other because they were said one after the other. Was it coincidence? Was it Providence? The fact is that no one knew the petition of the man next to him, we took our places as we happened to come in, and the "yes" and the "no" came one after the other. Was it coincidence? Was it Providence?

Your omnipotence and our omnipotence, We beseech You, hear us.

That You would vouchsafe to let us ever live the dogma of the Communion of Saints, We beseech You, hear us.

That You would vouchsafe to let us never forget that You make us priests of Your Church and for Your Church, We beseech You, hear us.

That You would vouchsafe to let our bodies and souls be instruments tuned to Your voice and Your miracle, We beseech You, hear us.

That You would vouchsafe to continue having mercy on us, We beseech You, hear us.

That You would vouchsafe graciously to hear us, We beseech You, hear us.

Son of God, We beseech You, hear us.

Christ, hear us.

Christ, graciously hear us.

Christ, have mercy on us.

Lord, have mercy on us.

After the litany we fell silent for a few minutes, thinking that at that moment we would go up to the altar one after another and the Bishop would impose his hands upon us. It would be *the* moment.

Then we stood up and sang the hymn *Veni Creator* asking the Holy Spirit to come upon us in these months that are left. Afterwards, at the moment of the consecration of the hands, we read a moving prayer we had composed ourselves.

80

O, Lord!

You who know intimately the history and geography of our poor hands, hear today the prayer we raise through them.

You, who for all eternity have dreamed of the day they were going to elevate You;

You, who have seen them new-born, trembling and defenseless;

You, who have smiled on seeing them loaded with toys, who have delighted on seeing them sunk deep in the hands of our mothers;

You, who have seen them raised to You in our first prayers and pressed to our breasts on the day of our first Communion;

You, who have wept to see them lose control for the first time and then have joyously seen them writhe with anger in the confessional;

You, who from Your Tabernacle, have seen them reach out towards You, sweat and shake in moments of youthful struggle;

You, who know our trembling when we touched the paten for the first time and when we opened the Tabernacle on the first day of our diaconate;

You, who see the devotion and reverence with which we look at them now, who know how we already feel they are something divine, something no longer ours;

You, who are soon going to find Yourself at home in them;

You, Lord.

In these few days that remain before Your coming,

let these unworthy hands make ready not to hurt You, so that when You are in them You long for Your Mother's hands as little as possible.

But You well know how small we are; You well know how useless are our efforts if You do not throw Yourself on them with all Your infinite omnipotence.

Then, Lord, bless, consecrate and sanctify these hands that we tremblingly lift up to You so that all they bless may be blessed and all they consecrate be consecrated and sanctified in the name of Your Son, our Lord, who lives and reigns in the union of the Holy Spirit, God world without end. Amen.

While Eugenio was reading the prayer in all our names there was a tense atmosphere in the chapel and I think it would have been possible to single out the breathing of each of us. Afterwards, we were silent for a moment—we were all pressing our hands together—and finally we sang the *Te Deum,* feeling a bit like priests already.

The whole thing only lasted a half hour, but it was very intense. We were all very happy when we left.

The holiday ended with a magnificent supper at which joy flowed abundantly.

A little while ago—it is 10 P.M.—I put the number 76 on the counter (I am the one in charge of changing the numbers every night). Another day is gone. I mean, one day less remains.

JANUARY 3—This morning, on the bus on our way back from a walk—we were packed in like sardines—a girl got on with six balloons, each of them larger than she. She shouted, *"Che macello!"* ("What a slaughterhouse!") We all expected the balloons to burst at any moment and awaited the crying that would follow. The people pressed together so as not to break them, as if they were a sick person, and the girl looked at her balloons with anguish. Her big sister couldn't help laughing and commented with little shrieks on the flood of people at each curve.

I am still amazed at the solidarity of the people. The entire bus riveted its attention on the balloons. And when I got off at the corner of the Corso, the six balloons—what a miracle!—were still buoyantly on their way.

JANUARY 6—Noon. This morning I was really disappointed when I sprang out of bed after the alarm went off and found that the shoes I had placed at my door were empty. "At least there could've been some candy. . ." Nothing. The Magi certainly haven't come through this year. Other times they would leave a calendar, a whistle, one of those lives of the Saints that nobody reads, but, after all, it was something and . . . to tell the truth, that's all we needed. The important thing was that the Magi existed. I have been in a bad mood all morning.

7 P.M.—The Magi must have changed their minds because today at dinner they placed their gifts at our plates. There was a pile of balloons and whistles. Everyone began to blow them and my ears still hurt. It was also wonderful to see Manzanares—our most revered and esteemed lawyer—walking with a balloon tied to his little finger. I think we priests are the people who come closest to being children. (I don't know why the devil this occurs to me now. Besides, it probably isn't very true. Unfortunately.)

JANUARY 10—There is something special about the dome of St. Peter's today that makes it appear different from usual. The sun shining behind it gives it a transparent look, as though it were made of alabaster. Moreover it seems to have lost all feeling of volume and looks cut out of cardboard. I suddenly think that perhaps they have taken it to the repair shop and have put up a temporary one of papier-maché so that no one notices the difference.

JANUARY 11—Today, the Feast of the Holy Family, we have had a little ceremony to pay homage to the Rector of the College. It was a very lively affair. The family atmosphere here is really tremendous. I don't know what people would think about our "sprees" but I could swear that I have never seen more genuine happiness. Our eyes all shine in a fashion that immediately gives away the particular brand of happiness of each of us.

JANUARY 16—This afternoon before beginning the rosary the Rector told us that a Jesuit priest had apostatized in Rome. Apparently the Communist papers published a long article of his this afternoon in which he says that in Communism he has found true faith.

84

The Rector almost cried when he told about it and a whip of emotion ran through the chapel. Afterwards we said the rosary better than ever, almost shouting. It was something to hear how people emphasized "Pray for us sinners" and "Lead us not into temptation."

When we finished we all ran out to buy *Il Quotidiano* to see the report, but it doesn't say much. It was said that he was a professor at the Gregorian University, but it can't be true because none of us know him.

Tonight we all talked about the affair. And it is strange that, just as earlier we had all shouted our prayers, now the tone of the conservations in the dining room was lower than ever. As if there were something overhead that kept us from talking.

JANUARY 17—Today we have had more news, although not very concrete. It seems that he is a priest of forty odd years who had been a Jesuit for only a short time since apparently he was converted at 23. Until that age, at which he made his first Communion, he had led an indifferent life, with no religious formation whatever.

He actually did live in the Gregorian University, but he was not a professor and only taught a religion course for lay people that is given there.

Everyone has something different to say as to the reason for this change.

Be that as it may, the fact is that it is a sad thing for Christ and for the Church. All day today I have been able to think of nothing else and have meditated on "lost"

85

priests. I am amazed how many people who call themselves Christians delight in speaking of these things and frivolously stir up these scandals, when they are so enormously distressing. The man who does not show compassion for them in this tragedy of theirs, the hardest blow they can receive, cannot be said to love Christ or the Church. Because if profaning a Host is something that is terribly distressing, often the profaner does not know what he is doing; but a host (and that is what a priest is) profaning itself is something which cannot be humanly understood. Although it is true that pride and the flesh weigh heavily on a man.

I ask myself what the causes of these falls can be and I see that pride is almost always at the bottom of them. I remember the very distressing case we studied a month ago of the apostasy of Lamennais. It was one of the few times that a wave of real emotion ran through one of my classes. We all held our breath when Father Grisar spoke of his brother's attempts to convert him on his deathbed. And you could actually hear the gasps in the class when the professor read what Jean Marie de Lamennais said when he heard of the death of his brother: "Felician, Felician, where are you?"

I think of the state of convulsion of the soul of a priest who is estranged from the Church and I remember the figure of the "married" priest in Graham Greene's novel who knows that, in spite of everything, he *is* a priest.

JANUARY 18—This morning I have again meditated on the same thing as yesterday. It has made me shudder to think that it is *possible* for something similar to happen to me. I am a man and not exactly a saint. And it must not be easy to walk through mud without getting spotted.

Sixty days. I raised my eyes to Our Lady of Clemency —I saw her dimly through my tears—and asked her to help me in the days that remain, in the very few days that remain.

Later I remembered the prayer of the hero of *Boy* which ran more or less, "Tie me, Lord, and thus there will be no danger." I wonder if it would not be better to give our freedom to God once and for all; but we have to wear the yoke of being free even though it hurts us. When I went to Communion I repeated fifteen or twenty times, "Lord, never permit me to be separated from You."

10 P.M. Going back to what I thought this morning, I decided on the motto for the ribbon that will bind my hands at the ordination. I wrote to my sister today and sent her the sketches and the motto. It will be five feet long and, along it, the sentence "Tie me, Lord, and I will eternally be Yours," in Latin. In the first letter of the words there will be five large medallions: The Sacred Heart, Our Lady, a Crucifix, a deacon holding the Eucharist, and, in the first one, some angels sounding trumpets as if summoning to joy. Now let's see how well she paints it.

JANUARY 20—Today as I was reciting the breviary, my heart jumped for joy when I read the scene in which Christ asks His disciples whom men say that He is. And as soon as I finished praying I came to my room and wrote on a bit of paper: "Christ curious about what they thought of Him."

This is consoling to me. I have wondered a great deal if my obsession for knowing what lay people think of us priests can come from pride. And now I am happy to find out that Christ must have been curious about it too. Although I'm not very sure that His reasons for asking are the same as the ones that underlie my worrying. Besides, He knew the answer before He asked; but, anyway, it pleases me to imagine Christ as being curious.

JANUARY 21—This afternoon we had Vespers in St. Peter's. It was a special thrill to kneel there in the midst of all that space and feel the warmth of the bones of the Apostle under my knees.

We were halfway through when a German pilgrimage came in, singing at the entrance (I wish Spaniards could sing like that). Afterwards they crowded about us, looking without saying a word. It made me feel that I knew them all; I don't know why it seems that I know everyone in the basilica, as if we were all from the same town.

JANUARY 22—Today I received letters from Santos and Cristóbal. It seems that I wrote an article in *Incunable*, commenting on what Gironella says about seminaries in *The Cypresses Believe in God*, and now these two seminarians tell me that I botched up my defense of the seminaries and that the worst part of it is that Gironella is right.

Santos says: *I have just read your article in "Incunable"*

discussing what Gironella has to say about seminaries and I wonder who is right. Gironella probably isn't very wrong. He is speaking about 1930. Judging by the peepholes that are still left in doors in the back corridors, by the stories in the "Correo Josefino" and the "good advice" they give us, we can deduce that his story is far from being a legend. The eternal problem of scandal would be another matter. But Gironella's ideas come out all right in the end, don't they? Let me tell you an anecdote that has something to do with this. Last year during the seminary support campaign, I was told to write a little article for the local newspapers. In spite of everything, I wrote it in the same style as all the others I see about the subject. Perhaps I stressed our happy side, likewise a hackneyed idea. (By the way, you know me and, well, you wouldn't hire me to advertise toothpaste through all eternity.) Anyway, I gave the article this title: "Boys in Cassocks." I even remember that I used these exact words: black stockings and shaved heads—rejecting them, naturally. Let me say first of all that I did not write sincerely. I couldn't do it both honorably and at the same time discreetly. I therefore almost defended the thesis of the "happy Indian." I ask you, what's the good of all this pretense? Wouldn't it be better to begin showing us as we really are, cautiously of course, and let everyone help us with their observations or their goading? As you see, I have torn down your house of cards with one stroke of the pen. . . Although the fact is that people are getting tired of our rose-colored glasses and our plaster. And then, the deceptions.

Yes, José Luis, I have worn stockings and had my head

shaved; I have gone hungry, I have suffered cold, I have played with rag and wool balls, etc., etc. Just until a few years ago the readers in my refectory read in a special sing-song. Look, two years ago I kept a diary but had to give it up after two months. It was very hard. And if I didn't fight, I only wrote dreams and drivel. I dare you to write your life in the seminary exactly as you have lived it, not as you would have liked it to be. You'll see. . . The mildest term you could decently use would be inmate of the poor-house . . . owl in the night of Astorga.

Santos goes on for a good while, because he is quite a talker. Cristóbal is more sparing of words, but he says the same thing: they all agreed with what Gironella had to say and they think that perhaps he did not go far enough. "Remember," he says, "that if I were to write a novel, it would be so clear that I would say many things that Gironella doesn't."

I read this letter with more sadness than joy, but now on re-reading it, it almost seems funny to me. I wonder if I'm a queer bird or if I wasn't just a poor blind kid, because the fact is that my novel of life in the seminary would not be so sad nor would I have ever dreamed of thinking of myself as living in a poor-house or as being an owl. And certainly, I speak with complete sincerity.

Now, two months before becoming a priest, when I look back over my thirteen years of studies, more than anything I have an impression of happiness. I don't know if it is because the beauty of this hour that I am living transfigures everything and leads to me believe that this joy more than makes up for all the suffering, or because the suffering simply did not exist.

Of course there were things to complain about in the seminary. I can see many of them and the article I sent to *Incunable* mentioned a few (quite a bit toned down by the censor), but I do not think that I would have come across fewer anywhere else.

I have never had my head shaved (although, in fact, they left us so little hair that it could scarcely be seen; but you ought to have seen how proud we were of our fine manes!). I never wore black stockings either. Only now do I play with rag balls (because we play soccer on the terrace and if they bounced they would go into the street and there would be no way of replacing them). Yes, I was cold, but perhaps there are very few people in the world who never are. We also went a bit hungry, and the worst thing was not that they gave us little to eat but that what they gave us was unpalatable.

Yes, certainly, it cannot be said that in my first years the seminary was a school for the nobility, but I assure you that I had a fine time and today it would seem ridiculous to me to judge the seminary by the pile of obscure details that are indisputably true.

Nowadays I do not think that Spanish seminaries are in general any worse than the average Institute. There will always be stern superiors, people who don't understand us and sometimes make us cry, and neither will we lack old, half-ruined buildings.

Yes, friend, yes; although you may not believe it, I was a happy man in the seminary. Perhaps I was unimpressionable, but I was happy and I have no reason for inventing a tragedy now. I cried a few times, but life is like that and one always has to vent his rage on somebody. The boys outside used to talk to us of the funereal Institutes in which they really spent wonderful years and we proclaimed our status as owls. That's life too.

Oh, no. I am not defending the thesis of the happy Indian nor do I think that the fact that priests are educated to sanctify justifies the hallways being dark or the desks in the classrooms uncomfortable, but I do believe that no matter how much we have we will always go on dreaming that we are martyrs. Besides, it is a pretty role to play. And cheap.

And now you are going to let me preach you a sermon. Confound it, we spend our lives talking about the poor and the disinherited and afterwards we shudder at lentils. When I went into the seminary I was almost a spoiled brat and I would cry in the dining room every day. Today I wouldn't object to eating any poor beggar's tasteless beans. And some day the salvation of a soul may very well depend on my doing it!

And now I want to tell you that you cannot imagine how distasteful it is for me to speak of these trifles just two months before I become a priest. This happiness I enjoy now would make up for fifteen years of prison. And for much more if there is no prison. It would take me a long time to add up all the joys I have had in the seminary, the fine friends I have found and the understanding superiors it has been my good fortune to come upon.

Let me tell you now of the solid education they have

given us. Yes, I know we are both afraid of hackneyed ideas; I know that people cackle a lot about our famous education. Still, after all is said and done, I assure you that I consider it much deeper than ordinary lay people's and I believe it takes much less effort on our part than on theirs. Perhaps at bottom we really have to form ourselves, but in the seminary one finds—and I have found—a very propitious atmosphere. The bad part is that scarcely do we leave the seminary when we put away our books, rub our hands and think: now I am a man. And even so, you still come across wonderful priests who make you stop and think. Almost all of them lack that polish, that command of words which one often acquires from leafing through magazines and reading a few novels. Perhaps this is why we make less of an impression than they. Aside from this inferiority complex which makes us think that our ideas are not worth being made known. How many sermons have I heard that are much more profound than many books you see floating (although, indeed, how poorly expressed. . . !)

I also want to speak to you of joy. I don't know outside atmospheres too well, but I sincerely believe that my classmates are the happiest young men I have every met. It was true that it was a happiness *sui generis,* the kind that does not make a rumpus but that does always leave a good taste. The priests' sadness comes later, when they feel they are alone, and not a few turn sour. Yes, dear Santos, I think that it is here one has to fight the great battle. *It is not he who can who is happy but he who wants.* What makes one happy is not fine food, but peace of the

93

spirit. And this peace of the spirit—this knowing that God is at our side—is what we must intensify now when life within the four walls of the seminary is so easy. Afterwards comes life and it is a sad sorrow to come across all those bitter priests who seem unhappy about their priesthood. And this is not, cannot be true.

JANUARY 25—Today I was reciting my breviary in the Gallery of the Pillar when people started to come back from class. I had just recited Sext and I closed the book for a few minutes before beginning None. I was walking with my hands crossed behind my back when I saw Mauricio's baby in the middle of the patio. He was lying on the chair—he cannot sit up alone yet—waving his little arms and feet in the air.

A group of students came in then and I began to observe the reactions of each of them. Morales started to run towards the infant as soon as he saw him and stayed there for four or five minutes, playing with him and letting himself be scratched. Pepe and Julio Manuel went to him for a minute and snapped their fingers but did not stop. Esteban passed by without looking at him and I noticed that he almost struggled not to turn his eyes (he is too good and now he has taken it into his head to be scrupulous). Then José Mari came and picked him up in his arms, put his hat on him and tried to make him walk (he is six months old and doesn't even know how to put out his foot). Then Sebastián and Robles also passed by without really noticing him and I don't think Méndez who was running—as usual—even saw him.

The spectacle amused me and then, as soon as a fellow came through the door, I would say: this one will stop, this one will pass by, this one will wink at him but without stopping. It was almost a game and I guessed right most of the time.

I have observed that in general it is embarrassing for many of us young priests to play in public with little children. At least that is what happens to me; at home I play with my nephews and I am more of a child than they. But outside it is torture for me to put on a serious face and not pick them up or fondle them. I realize that it is stupid because people probably understand perfectly well, but there is something, something strange and inexplicable that embarrasses me.

When the bell rang I had still not begun None.

JANUARY 28—It seems impossible that it is winter. The sun is shining and Rome is taking on that "color of autumn leaves" Valverde talks about. I think that this afternoon has perhaps been transplanted from spring. An army platoon is going down the street to the rhythm of a military march that has lost in the afternoon sun any warlike quality it might have had. I repeat Guillén's line, "The world is well-made," and Rosales', "and everything marks time in joy."

Then, to reaffirm the idea, I went up to the terrace but I came running down because I couldn't stand the noise of the Vespas. The world may be well made, but motors aren't.

JANUARY 30—*Letter to God asking for a miracle.*

Dear God,

The reason for this letter I'm writing you today is an odd one. I don't write letters asking for miracles every day.

But the truth is that it is just a little miracle and so I think that my audacity will not surprise you too much. I simply want to ask you that the city wake up covered with snow at dawn on St. Joseph's Day.

You laugh? I really mean it. I'm not looking for symbolism or mysteries. It would be very nice if all the purity on earth gathered about me that day, but I only ask it of you in an ingenuously romantic way. When I open the window, it would be so magnificent to remember all my old life in the snow.

I have not seen snow for five years and that is too long a time. I don't know if there was snow in Nazareth when you were a child, but you surely remember how we love all the things which played an important part in our childhood. And for me perhaps the most representative memory of my early years is the city of Astorga just after a snowstorm.

Going out in the morning on the way to the seminary when the first bells were ringing and finding the street immaculate, just created and new, all for us. For us: for my mother and for me.

"Follow in my footsteps, son."

And we marched along—one, two; one, two; one, two; —footprint over footprint. Afterwards, when the first neighbors came out, no one would guess who had walked by or imagine what shoes could have that strange shape, with a woman's heels and a child's taps.

I laugh to think what you will say on hearing me tell all these that you know better than I. But they are things that I have to say. Or I'll burst. Besides, who knows if you won't be touched and end up granting me the miracle? It is a very simple thing to boot; with all the miracles you will perform that day, what effort would just one more take?

That's all. Goodbye.

Love,

José Luis

P. S. Now I seem to remember that the idea is not very original. And I am even quite sure that St. Thérèse of Lisieux asked it on the day of her profession. Or of her first Communion, I don't remember. And God granted it to her. Of course, St. Thérèse was St. Thérèse and I . . . I sincerely believe that there is no danger of God granting me this miracle. The ecclesiastic authorities can relax.

FEBRUARY 1—I've finally received the age dispensation! I did not really think it wouldn't arrive, for I never doubted that it would come on time—although without any reason, I understand, because it could just as well not have come— but, at any rate, I breathe more freely now.

Above all I am happy for Uncle Paco. It seems incredible how Providence arranges things: my first Mass will coincide exactly with the 50th anniversary of his. I remember how moved we were when we realized what an extraordinary coincidence this is going to be. In his last letter he said that this is to be his relief, but I am going to write him and say that it is not so, that it is the *alternativa**. He is the bull-fighter in the plenitude of power who opens the way to the novice, but without retiring from the arena himself.

I was moved when I thought that he will be at my right at my first Mass and when I say, "I will go unto the altar of God," it will be he who answers, "To God, who giveth joy to my *youth*."

FEBRUARY 3—The other day Angel and I talked about the pessimism and the optimism of the priest. I remember now how sententiously I used to talk of these things when I was studying Philosophy and would write poems in which I rhymed "enthrall" with "gall," "relief" with "grief" and "divine" with "pine". And still these are not things to be fooled with.

Where is the world headed today? What course will it take? What is to become of us? Thank God, we cannot know the future. It would be horrible.

I told Angel that I sincerely believe that martyrdom is our only way out, that our ordination is almost like a contract for them to shoot us four years from now. The world cannot go on this way. There is no doubt that we are

---

* The ceremony by which a recognized bull-fighter formally authorizes a novice to kill bulls in the ring with other recognized *toreros*. R.G.

moving ahead to a new era; a new world is dawning, it is going to emerge at any moment and we do not know if it will bear the sign of God or of the devil. What we do know is that the final victory is to be ours.

If people would only understand that we are going through crucial times, everything would be easier and the new world could even be born without labor. But I am afraid that the solution will be a great catastrophe, a new invasion of the barbarians that will reduce to ashes the western world, as empty as it is proud. But perhaps these are the ways of God and, as sixteen centuries ago, the conquered will again triumph over the conquerors and Malenkov, or whoever it may be, will be the new Clovis. Yes, it may well be that a new Middle Ages will be born to the world then, a new Christian era under the sign of justice.

But to achieve it many martyrs will be needed. And, of course, we priests will not be the last to die. Yet perhaps this martyrdom is too pretty. Oh, that other one, that everyday martyrdom . . . !

FEBRUARY 5—Today, I don't know why, I have written some epigrams about my first Mass.

When one holds a Host against the light, he must necessarily see God.

•

Priests should lose their sight after their first Mass.

99

I do not understand why musicians have not made the bell a solo instrument in the orchestra.

•

The candles of the last Mass that is said in the world will burn for all eternity, like the bush of Moses.

•

The missal bursts with envy of priests. It knows all the words, but cannot say them.

•

Priests who die while they are saying Mass will not be judged immediately, because the Mass cannot be interrupted. They will end it in Heaven (they couldn't finish it in Hell) and then they will have to stay there because one cannot leave Heaven.

•

Before making Adam's fingers, God must have practiced a great deal so that the Host would look artistic when held in the hands.

•

Water looks as though it were always in a hurry and only with inner protests does it stop running. If I could, I would always travel by water. Someone has already said that many are the drops which flow, but only one reaches the chalice.

•

If there were bells on God's cloak as on those of the

priests of Israel, we would hear Him shake at the Consecration.

●

Tears cried from rage in the Old Testament; they felt useless. On Holy Thursday night they realized that they had a purpose.

●

The night fights desperately with the dawn, because it always wants to stay to hear Mass. But the dawn is such a glutton that it wants them all for itself. Only at Christmas can it be happy and it stays to hear three Masses, one after the other.

●

At all the doors and windows of churches there ought to be an angel who would not let noises in until all the Masses were over.

●

If it were not for multilocation, the body of Christ would always protest. The telephone of heaven does not leave Him alone, because every minute they call Him from another altar.

●

The altar-stone also had its annunciation: "And blessed art thou among stones."

●

When Adam invented the first system of numbers, he could not even have dreamed that numbers would be used for something as sacred as counting the Masses that one has said.

101

FEBRUARY 7—In the Piazza Tritone we were caught by one of the worst downpours I have seen in Rome. Everyone ran to a doorway and even the traffic policeman left his post. They were wonderful minutes. As they bounced, the drops fashioned a magic spectacle of crystal stalagmites. The piazza looked like a lagoon. When a car passed, it left two tracks as deep as river beds which the drops later erased.

I recalled how sad the rain used to make me a couple of years ago when I was at the peak of my romanticism. Today, the impression was quite different and, for a reason I still do not understand, I felt like laughing.

FEBRUARY 10—More and more I admire village priests. Maybe we have been a little poisoned by the novel and now admire *heroic* priests more than the others. I think that the priest in Bernanos' *Diary of a Country Priest* is not a country priest. Bernanos was right when he pointed boredom out as being the greatest torment of village priests; not *that* boredom, however, but a much more ordinary one. The priest of Ambricourt is really a hero, an extraordinary case; and excessive boredom becomes not boredom but suffering. The worst thing is that one scarcely realizes when he has been overcome by that kind of ennui. The worst thing about boredom is that one becomes bored without realizing it.

That is why I admire these little village priests who are always happy and seem as though they have just been baptized. They no longer have the fever for work they did at the beginning, which so often leads to slow waste and to foundering in a rut. But they do have a vision of life anchored in God which I would truly want for myself and all my classmates. Their apostolate is effortless and natural, as if they were already in the kingdom of heaven.

I think that we—the young priests of today—will perhaps never achieve this serenity. Maybe it is bad for them to paint us an heroic priest who makes a good novel or movie because then we discover that reality is very different.

I am consoled to think that all this depends on one's age and the kind of life he leads.

FEBRUARY 12—Antonio has just told me that he won't be ordained now. They have not granted him the age dispensation. I have been sad all afternoon because he had his heart set on it. I think he is going through exactly the same thing that I did last year. Perhaps one always has to suffer.

FEBRUARY 15—Today I discussed priests in novels with Mariano for more than two hours. I am amazed to see that Spanish priests who speak of this subject always refer only to Bernanos' *Diary of a Country Priest* and perhaps to Cesbron's *Saints in Hell*.

This vision is no doubt very incomplete and I understand why they have not made a good impression in Spain, especially if one believes that Bernanos meant that priests are "like this" or even that "they should be like this," things which did not even cross his mind.

The vision would be more complete if we studied the different groups of books about priests: the black ones (Bernanos, Coccioli, Cesbron, Joannon); the white ones (Marshal, Trese, Merton); the red novels (Greene); and the rose-colored ones (Robinson).

I wonder what the reason for this avalanche of novels about priests can be. The answer is quite clear: because priests are interesting, or perhaps because the religious problem is interesting and the novelist sees in the priest the model of the hero who lives out the religious problem with the most intensity. But, isn't there a grain of truth in what Alvarez de Miranda, writing in *Revista* (I think), says about this being the index of the irreligiousness of the day? It is true that in the periods of greatest religiousness the priest was an otherwordly being, admired, but never put under the microscope. What was interesting about the priest was what there was in him of a representative of God; one never thought about him as a human being fit for analysis. In order for the priest's human nature to be accentuated, it is necessary for religion to decline.

But which of the two visions is more complete? There is something of God and something of man in a priest; stressing either one of the two extremes to the detriment of the other means disfiguring his real personality. Is it less religious to study Christ as a man than to see and admire Him as God? And now the last question: Are the religions which view God as being distant and unattainable more truly religious than Christianity, which feels Him in its hand and knows that He is of our race? To tell the truth, I'll take the second.

FEBRUARY 17—Carnival always makes me sad. They are evil days. And ridiculous. For one day farce goes without a mask, farce unveiled and in full view of all.

We had a Holy Hour in reparation for all the sins that would be committed in Rome today and I was half-abstracted. What a fine way to make reparation! If the days rang like bells, these days would sound hollow, false, like bells made of tinfoil.

FEBRUARY 18—I am happy in spite of the gravity of the date: Ash Wednesday. The ceremony of the imposition of ashes gave me a very different impression this year than in the past. When the Rector applied them to my forehead ("Remember, man, that thou art dust and to dust thou shalt return.") I translated: "Remember, José Luis, that thou art dust and Christ thou shalt become." Then, on returning to my place, I could scarcely hold back my inopportune laughter. I repeated the sentence to myself throughout the entire ceremony and each time I felt like jumping in my seat. Then I corrected it a bit and added, "Remember that thou art dust and Christ they shalt make thee." Yes, because the whole transformation will come from without and all I will have to do is stand still. I thought: like the flour in the oven or the meat in the nut, God will ripen and cook me; I will only have to let Him do it, and be quiet and stand still. I had the impression that four or five magic wands were flying over my head. And I thought: Open, sesame.

I am definitely happy.

Yesterday we put the number 30 on the stairway. Before we only put it in our Common-room and now it has jumped to the two stairways because the ordination is a holiday not only for those who are being ordained but also for the whole college. Whenever I go up and down, I go out of my way in order to see it twice. And, when I am alone, I pass by and caress the numbers. Afraid, lest they see me and laugh.

FEBRUARY 20—I still dream about sliding down the bannister on the stairway to the dining room. It is impossible for me to go down alone without being tempted to do it. But I still have never done it.

I remember that a few years ago I thought about writing a movie script about the life of the seminarian and one of the characters—naturally!—was myself. And this was the introduction of this fellow:

"The camera placed at the top of the stairs photographs a seminarian who whistles as he goes down. Suddenly he stops. He looks up and, on seeing that there is no one coming, he climbs onto the bannister and . . . whee . . . all the way to the bottom."

Who knows, maybe I'll do it tomorrow. The bad thing will be if the bannister breaks, for it is probably not very used to such strains; although I do not think it will. I have already tested its safety more than once. Of course, I have been doing this for five years now and I still have not dared to. . . whee. . .

FEBRUARY 25—It is strange to go to class every morning when you await such enormous things. But, basically, it seems wonderful to me that God comes into us without clamor, little by little, while we walk our usual way to the university.

What I will never be able to help is surprising myself on occasion abstractedly thinking about what awaits me, while Father Kempf speaks of Charlemagne with impressive gravity. Ah! Did Charlemagne really exist?

FEBRUARY 26—Re-reading this diary I see that on the 15th of this month I say that, all in all, the novel faithfully portrays priests as they are, but today I think that this is too flattering an affirmation. I ask myself if I truly understand priests, and, of necessity, I have to say no; the closer I draw to the priesthood, the more incomprehensible they become to me.

For some time now I have not been able to see one of my classmates who is a priest without having 15 or 20 questions leap into my mind: How are they different from me and the rest of men? What is there about their hands that mine do not have? And why do a few of their words work miracles while the same words are but a pantomime when said by me?

And, in spite of everything, I *know* that it is not the same, and it would seem a sacrilege to me to compare my rehearsals with their Masses.

I remember now that sentence of the Curé of Ars: "The priest will only be understood in heaven."

Yes, perhaps that is it. Perhaps in heaven priests will wear a red cross on their breasts and souls and show it to everyone as the most glorious of decorations.

FEBRUARY 27—I went to the catacombs of St. Callistus with Fidel today to reserve the altar of the Popes for him for March 20. I felt something odd when we took the bus; I thought that the next time I went over that route I would be a priest. We looked at each other and I realized that he was thinking the same thing.

When we signed up, the man in charge told us that on the 19th on that same altar a Salesian was going to celebrate the 75th anniversary of his first Mass. Fidel and I looked at each other, startled. As soon as we left, I took a pencil and multiplied: 27,375 Masses.

"And 18 leap years," said Fidel.

"And three Masses on Christmas and All Souls Day."

"And the binations . . . "

"Almost 30,000 Masses . . . !"

"I'm going to be afraid to celebrate my first afterwards . . . "

We walked home through the pines. We scarcely spoke all the way.

MARCH 1—I received a letter from home that made me laugh; they are all mad as hatters. They all say the same thing and in the same words. I am sorry I have not kept the letters my mother has written me in these past months to prove that they are all the same; they write me often now, almost twice a week, and the only thing they do is say over and over how they are going to thank God.

Lolita tells me that my mother spends the day crying, that she is knitting and that she sits wrapped in thought, without moving, for four or five minutes. She and Crucita keep still and the three of them end up crying.

MARCH 2—I am amazed to see that I still have not said anything in this diary of Our Lady of Clemency when she is my obsession these days. I never believed that one could become so fond of a specific image. She is before my desk now and only looking at her makes me smile.

I don't know, perhaps it would be better not to say anything. I won't know how to talk about her. It is always more difficult to express happiness than sorrow. When one is sad he runs to tell it to someone, or to write it if he is a poet. But our joys beg to be shouted and jumped over rather than to be written about. And I cannot doubt for a single instant that my greatest joy these days is looking at Our Lady.

MARCH 3—Today I began to really practice the Mass. I never thought it would be so complicated, full of infinite details: bowing the head, kissing the altar, joining and opening the hands. . . . And, nevertheless, each thing has its explanation and is beautiful. I am amazed that our Masses do not seem as artistic as the best of performances.

MARCH 4—Gonzalo tells me that his greatest torture is the murmuring in the chapel during Mass. There are sixty priests in the house and, since the first class begins very early, at eight-thirty, they have to say Mass in three shifts of twenty. There is a chapel for them that we call the basilica; it is a hallway with little chapels to the right and left. Although they all try to say Mass in a low voice— and this must be very annoying—there is a very bother-some buzzing, in spite of the fact that we have done away with ringing the bells. It would be a fine frolic if we didn't!

I think it is going to be hard for me to say Mass softly; when you hear the words, they seem more profound.

At any rate, it is marvelous that we have sixty Masses every day here in the house; if we pricked the walls a stream of holiness would come flowing out.

When we go to class—the streets still half-deserted— it is also good to think that we have already had our hour with God. Perhaps this is the most holy hour in the city. Once the hours of vice are ended, in Rome, God comes to 10,000 altars.

MARCH 5—I get all tangled up in my fingers. I am obsessed by the fact that, after the Consecration, you have to keep your index finger and your thumb together, and, sometimes, at dinner time or when I am studying, I surprise myself pressing my fingers together like a brute, almost hurting myself. I am not responsible for my hands these days.

MARCH 6—This afternoon it was nice on the terrace. It seemed as though there were less noise in the street, and on the neighboring terraces there were only a few maids laughingly shaking out some blankets. Then, when it got dark, there was even less noise and the bells of St. Augustine's were heard clear and limpid, without that rat-a-tat of cars and Vespas which so often makes me flee from the terrace.

When it was completely dark, I closed my breviary and began to review the prayers of the Mass, although I already know them by heart. It is not necessary to learn them all because that is what the missal is for, but I prefer to learn them since otherwise it is a mess to keep track of both the book and the altar cards.

These prayers of the Mass have a special charm, different from that of all the others. I said them with my eyes closed and my hands crossed behind my back and I felt satisfied, complete. They are short, exact, almost dry. They say what they have to say and they say it without being flowery. I think that if I had to compose "my" Mass, I would have made them much more complicated. I am not stupid enough to consider myself capable of making them more beautiful; now even the word "beautiful" sounds strange to me. Yes, there is no doubt that it is much better for them to be so simple and elemental, since they do not lack flavor because of this and, at the same time, are good for everyone. Then again, when he says them, although he uses the same words, each priest says a different prayer, stressing this word or that or giving his own personal meaning to each phrase. And so, using the self-same formulae, each one speaks to God in his own words.

They have another advantage: they avoid sentimentality without closing the door on it. It would be a fine thing if the Mass were like those saccharine prayers you come across in prayer books!

MARCH 7—Today, after practicing the Mass, a very strange thing struck me. It seemed to me that the form I had used for the rehearsal shouted to me and said: "Ever since I was born in the grain, I always dreamed of becoming the body of Christ; I dreamed of the mill, of the sack and, finally, I saw my dreams about to come true when they cut me out to go to the altar. And now, suddenly, you take me and deceive me; you do everything just as if you were going to perform the miracle but, at the moment of the Consecration, I hold my breath waiting to become Christ and, all at once, I understand that you do not use the *tone* that priests do, that your words are not like theirs, and that within me everything is the same. And afterwards, you divide me, you consume me and . . . goodbye forever to the dream of my life. For you this rehearsal will be happy, but for me it has been a tragic one."

MARCH 8—This morning I thought how differently I act when I serve Mass now than before. Now I am always alert and pay attention to all the details so as to learn to say it myself. I think this inquisitorial peering of mine must bother the priest. Now all details interest me, and I have noticed defects in the way he performs the ceremonies that I never saw before. For example, he looks at the Crucifix all through the Offertory when he should only look at it for a moment and then lower his eyes to the paten.

But, all in all, he says Mass well and with true devotion. Perhaps he lacks a bit of humanity in the ceremonies which seem a little rigid; but this is a matter of character and he probably cannot help it.

MARCH 9—Now that I am learning how to say Mass, it hurts me more than ever when I see a priest who says it too fast. When the ceremonies are performed inelegantly they seem caricatures and almost mockery.

I like making a rite of even the simplest things, like the greeting *Dominus vobiscum* (which basically is no more than "Good day" or "God keep you") which is performed slowly, almost like a Japanese salutation. If we really made the most of all these ceremonies, I haven't the least doubt that the faithful—and we— would feel that God was nearer and more tangible. I will always remember the sad look on don Pablo's face when he told us what an English girl had written to her brother in London: "You tell me to be careful not to be influenced by the atmos-

113

phere in Spain and become a Catholic. Don't worry. If you saw how Catholic priests say Mass, you wouldn't be afraid of my being converted."

This is no doubt an exaggeration—and, moreover, the defects of its ministers have nothing to do with the truth of a religion—but it is a fact that sometimes they say Mass as if it were just another job. (It frightens me to think that some day I may say it that way.)

MARCH 10—*Afternoon.* At dinner Antonio read us a proclamation that was as good as the one he read Christmas Day. We listened to him in complete silence and there was something indefinable in the air.

Proclamation on *the* Eve of Ordination

Brothers
we announce to you the greatest joy of the year!
Now the cone comes to a point
now the firmament hastens towards the keystone
now the calendar has only red numbers of a single digit
now the numbers approach three
two
one
now it seems that only union with the one is the most
    formidable of all truths.
Brothers
if it were not Lent. . .
if it were not true that not even epics are worthy of the
    priesthood. . .

114

if it were not true that here it is not a question of procla-
mations but of identification with the cross of
Christ. . .
But in spite of everything
rejoice!
as the Virgin rejoiced and exulted
as the saints rejoiced and exulted on climbing the mount
of empty roads, without roads
as all creatures twist with exultant joy when the Trinity
elevates them
because then the stalk is completely snapped
and the very breaking of being is essential joy.
Thus
rejoice and exult
because there is come the day of total shattering,
of absence of self,
of not mattering to ourselves and of nothing mattering
any longer
the mere "us"
to no one
because we matter only in the light of eternal God.
Rejoice: in the sea of nothingness we are creatures
Rejoice: in the sea of creatures we are men
Rejoice: in the turbid lagoon of humanity we are Christians
Rejoice: in the standing lake of Christianity we are priests.
Priests! Priests! Priests!
Can you want anything more?
Now that I know what it is, can anyone want anything
else?

Priests! Priests! Priests!
Christ prolonged in 300,000 consecrated men.
Christ mercifully transferred in three hundred thousand
    paradoxical men!
In you the humility of Christ,
in you the obedience of Christ,
in you the charity of Christ,
the cross of Christ nailed to your backs.
Christ!!! Christ!!! Christ!!!
and all the rest are saved provided we are sons;
because there is only One made incarnate
and all the rest are saved by following His way to Divinity.
Because there is only one Man who was God, who in total
    blue meekness
with His eyes can tell all the afflicted to come to Him.
Rejoice and make men happy.
Go tell them to look high
                think deeply
                love madly
we have been saved by pure love.
Go to them with tempered word
with pen upraised.
through waves or through bars of iron and willow
in huts and in palaces
there where you find the most incipient rational
    animal.
Go and tell them that the idea of "rational animal" is
    past history, that now the only definition approved
    by the Teacher is "Children of God."
Go, but when you go, for God's sake, stay

when you speak, for God's sake, listen
when you preach, for God's sake, punish your bodies
when you give, for God's sake, enrich yourselves
when you open your hearts, for God's sake seal them and
    bolt them
when you are Christ, for God's sake, be Christ.
Christ, Christ, Christ.
Through Him, with Him, in Him.
That is all
through Him, with Him, in Him.
For all else is absurd
              mad
             vain.
For all that is not Christ tires
                     torments
                     darkens
                     benumbs
                     dirties
                     weakens
Christ! Christ! Christ!
You in Christ
Christ through you in others.
Christ! Christ! Christ!
So that when the Lord of glory comes
—who for now wants to continue coming to you only
    on a cross—
so that when He comes to forty pairs of tense eyes.
under forty pairs of imposed hands
He may find what He comes to give you:
Christ.

MARCH 10—Night. This afternoon we began the Spiritual Exercises. A week of the most absolute silence and solitude with God.

I need it. To rest in order to review my life and revise my ideas in the light of the mystery which is drawing near. A week to pray and pray and enjoy the Tabernacle. It will not leave my soul unmarked. Help me, Lord, to use it well.

(Here my diary grows longer and longer and less literary and becomes rather a dialogue. But I think I do not have the courage to transcribe it.)

THE HOUR FOR TEARS

AND SO, THE NIGHT OF THE 18TH ARRIVED. How will I
tell you all this? Can you possibly understand all the
emotion, all the joy of these moments? The hour for tears
had struck on the clock of my life. How long had it been
since I cried? I do not know exactly. Since my childhood
I had perhaps only really cried at the ordination of my
classmates a year before. Now, however, in the last months
before my ordination, I felt unhinged, and merely thinking about the 19th made tears come to my eyes. And
now, there it was, opening the door: the day for tears.

119

The first time I cried was when I put the 0 on the counter. I remember that I felt afraid to place it there. After dreaming about this moment for so long, now that it had arrived, it overpowered me. On other days, I preferred to change the numbers when everyone could see me, when there were the most people on the stairway. But that night I did not have the courage to do it. I waited until they had all gone up to their rooms and, as though I were going to commit a crime, I slipped down to put up the number. My hands trembled as I untacked the 1 and, when I put up the 0, I felt that my eyes were misted over with tears.

The superiors had told us to go to bed early; if not, someone might have spent the night in the chapel and would have been in a terrible state the next morning. But, even so, the lights must have been turned off very late in our rooms.

When I closed my door, I thought that the next morning was going to be of a definitive, special nature for me. I thought: tomorrow, when I open the door, I will go out and be ordained. And also: tomorrow, when I polish my shoes, I will be a priest. And everything would be different tomorrow when I went to bed.

I do not know why I remember all this in such exact detail. I could retrace my steps one by one, the places I was, everything. It was as though I were hollow; I aimlessly strode back and forth in my room, as if in heaven they were working me on strings. I went to the window and looked at the stars for a long while as I said Hail Marys with absolutely no concept of time.

120

I sat down at my desk and began to write in the diary I had begun three months earlier and which was ending now. I laugh today—and I am moved—when I read the page that I wrote then: full of repetition—how many times I write the word "finally!"—strangely choppy, jumping from one idea to another without any continuity at all.

Finally. In a few minutes, when I finish writing these lines, I will go to bed. It will take me some time to fall asleep, but I will fall asleep. Afterwards, I will wake up and we will already be on the other shore, on the shore of Christ. Tomorrow the dawn's first music will be the beginning of my priesthood. I will wake to another day, consecrated.

I am tired now, but I am happy. I am infinitely happy. I know it is futile for me to attempt to express my sentiments. My head is heavy with joy and all I can do is repeat the same thing over and over again: I am happy, I am happy, I am terribly happy.

I have the impression now of being a condemned man who is writing his last words. Something really is going to die in me. Tomorrow little, childish, naive José Luis will have died. The boy will wake up to another, much greater reality which will make the child of bygone days burst. Something very great is going to be born in me.

As I write these lines, they are talking outside my door. On my wall I hear the stapler, the one we use for putting up posters. Tomorrow the corridor will be com-

pletely different, full of pictures and music. And we, Lord, how different we will be! Perhaps this is the idea that staggers me most these days: everything will be the same and everything will be different.

Everything will be the same. We will have the same idiosyncrasies, do the same things, have the usual temptations and the self same lapses. Everything will be the same. People will see us on the street the same as they did yesterday and just as they will tomorrow.

Everything will be different. This is the great truth, the truth that tonight makes me tremble with joy to think how right it is that, in spite of everything, I will no longer be the same and all that sameness will be true and yet also false, because Christ will be in my words, in my hands, in everything I have.

It is a question of faith, of believing that everything will be true and not just another pretty story, or rather it will be a true story, the kind that should be resurrected when our enormous, deceitful world is gone. Mysteries can be seen; tomorrow I will see this mystery of feeling You at my side, physically visible. Everything will tell me that it is true. And though I may marvel I will not be able to doubt that what I have in my hands are indeed miracles. Now nothing will be impossible for me, because Christ will be with me, and my words have new meaning. I know that I will really bless now, that my blessing will be that of the Lord, that I will really bless in the Name of the Father and of the Son and of the Holy Ghost. IN HIS NAME.

How can I tell men this truth which is so clearly

visible? How few are those who understand it, and even we are slow and tardy of heart! Lord, increase my faith; let me believe in You without seeing You, but, just in case, touch my heart so that I may truly know You.

At this time of night, all sorts of sins are probably being committed in the world. In Rome. And I await the coming of God to my soul. I should like Your coming into my soul to make You forget all this, all this filth that infests our lives.

Today all my desires are fulfilled. After so many years of waiting, we finally attain our goal. Tonight I put 0 on the counter. Many dreams were needed for it to take place. It is always like this, time. Thirteen years ago now, I began to go to the seminary on those cold December mornings with my coat pulled up to my ears and following in my mother's footsteps until we reached the Plaza de Higiene where she would kiss me and go off to hear Mass at St. Martha's while I went into Carbon Square, towards the seminary, turning my head many times until finally my mother was lost from sight in one of the innumerable turns on the Street of the Serpent. All this is now culminating; on this luminous St. Joseph's morn, it is all going to come into being.

Tomorrow Handel's "Hallelujah Chorus" will burst forth in my soul like the voice of God stirring its innermost depths. I will say the Te Deum *as I get out of bed; I want to put all my child's soul into it for You, lodge in my glance all the love of my life, speak to You with the ingenuous words I should like to have today.*

Yes, I am living a half real, half poetically invented

123

childhood. It would be so splendid to go up to Your altar with a soul as bright and clear as the one I picture to myself . . . My story is short, but it is certainly not the one I would like to present to You. At any rate, becoming a child these days is the only way of being able to understand at least something of what is happening to me. It is so far removed from everything logical . . .

My hands, they obsess me.

Today I received a letter from my sister, the nun, which made me cry a lot. Dear God, unite her to all my works; it will be she who makes my priesthood fruitful.

If I were to reap even the slightest fruit from this retreat, it would be enough; I am speaking of genuine affection for my precious Lady of Clemency. She is going to light my priestly life. May it be as bright as Your smile.

I feel very tired. I am going to bed (it is twelve thirty already). Keep my sleep, oh, Lord, for today it is terribly sacred. I think now that I could die tonight. My God, it would be dreadful. Oh, no, no, I cannot possibly die this way . . . ! No, watch over my heart, stay very near so that not one of its beats is lost, and awaken me to a day full of sun, Your Sun.

When I had finished writing this, I went towards my bed. I tore the leaf with the 18 off the calendar and the red one of March 19, 1953 appeared. I drew near and kissed it; then I laughed at such a tasteless gesture. I got into bed and from there, with the light still on, I looked at that date for a long while; then I ran my eyes over the four walls of my room and I felt happy. I put my hands to my lips and kissed them almost voraciously. I was feeling happy when I turned out the light.

● ● ●

I was awake at half past three in the morning. It was still night and I stayed in bed. I tossed and turned without being able to fall asleep. I looked at the calendar. 19. Finally. However—I do not know why—I remember that I thought the day would not really begin until the loudspeaker burst out singing the "Hallelujah Chorus" which would give us the news: "Come on, the day has come. Now you can be happy."

Thus I waited in bed until they played it. A few minutes before six-thirty, the loudspeaker began to creak. I said: they are testing it. And now my heart really did begin to pound madly. I could hear it beat; it hurt me; I noticed that I was gasping and, when the music exploded from the loudspeaker, the first tears had already welled up in my eyes. Tremendously moved, I sat up in bed feeling something indefinable: a mixture of gratitude, joy, a sensation of sureness, of arrival, of coming into port, of having fulfilled everything. I felt how my tears fell on the sheets; it was a deep weeping, serene now. I rested my head on the pillow and let myself cry all through the "Hallelujah Chorus"; I believe I did not think about anything, but only cried.

125

I sprang out of bed. I washed and shaved. My crying stopped when I saw myself in the mirror, and I began to laugh when I saw how funny my face was, all full of tears and soap. I joyfully greeted my double in the mirror, and I even had the strength to scold him: "What a baby . . . !"

Meanwhile, the music was still echoing through all the halls. After the "Hallelujah Chorus" came the Hymn of the Pope played on silver trumpets and after it a Chorale and a Fugue by Bach. Finally, Somma's *Ave Maria*. Each of these pieces made my emotions jump from the bursting happiness of Handel, to the triumphant hymn —at this moment I remembered and saw so many ceremonies in the Vatican—and from there to the pious music of the chorale and the playful one of the fugue, ending with the sweetest of all prayers which I sang along with the loudspeaker.

When I opened my door, my eyes were struck by a large ☧ (Christ) and under it in red letters: TU ES SACERDOS IN AETERNUM (You are a priest forever), and my doorjamb was marked with a large red cross—two long strokes of blood—and some lines that said: JOSE LUIS: THE ANGEL OF GOD HAS PASSED OVER YOUR DOOR AND HAS MARKED IT. AFTER TODAY YOU WILL BE A PRIEST FOREVER.

I remembered the scene in the Bible in which the Jews marked their doors with the blood of a lamb, so that when the angel of death passed over the next morning only the houses which had the mark on their doors were freed from the horrible slaughter of the first-born.

126

Our doors were also marked now, with the sign of life, of the new life which was going to begin.

And I went down the hallway, stopping at each one of the doors that were marked with blood. At Cipriano's, at Mateo's, at Fidel's; at José María's, at Alfredo's . . . How our blood shook! How we felt ourselves called . . . with no doubts now! This sign brands us against the sword of death. The Sign on my door will wear off in four days perhaps, but in my soul it will last centuries, and centuries, and centuries, and centuries. It will endure through all eternity because we have been sealed by the blood of God, the blood of the Lamb who saves us.

They had decorated the entire house. The stairway was covered by parchments with all the biblical sentences relating to the priesthood, and, next to them, sketches of bells, churches, chalices . . . I went through the house enjoying seeing it as though I did not know it. I needed to walk, move, be calm.

Later I went to the chapel of the Priests, sat down in a corner and read the rite of ordination while, for the second time, I was overcome by tears. Angel was saying Mass and, on thinking that I would be doing the same thing two hours later, I felt a hand clutch at my throat. When he elevated his hands and the trembling Host appeared behind his head, I felt my nails dig into my palms. That was true, true, true.

I remember that I looked at my watch often in the hour that I spent there and, when it was seven-thirty, I ran out as if I were going to be late, and then I had to spend a half hour walking up and down the gallery to

127

kill time. Rolled up in my pocket, I had the ribbon painted by my sister that I had received the previous afternoon and which was going to bind my hands after the anointing. I was crushing it in my palm. My hands were perspiring.

It was a quarter to eight when we all went in to dress. There were eighteen of us, eighteen poor, shaking, pale, stuttering boys whose eyes shone with tears and whose hearts were filled with joy. They had to help us dress because we could not have managed alone. I remember exactly where it was. I shall never forget it. There we were, the eighteen of us, dressed in white, looking at each other without seeing, without recognizing each other; knowing that the time had come, that in a few minutes all would be fulfilled.

When we went out to the gallery, it was six minutes to eight. It was a clear morning and the sun shining in through the arches showed even whiter than our albs. In the courtyard, they were raising the Spanish flag next to the Pope's when the Bishop arrived.

We began to walk towards the church and I knew that now each step we took was a very serious thing: they were the steps which were leading us to Christ, which were taking us to die and be reborn.

The choir began to sing and all my emotion came to my throat: *Filioli mei,* they said, "My beloved children, behold, I am with you."

I could listen no longer. This indeed was the hour for tears. I walked forward, repeating; "Beloved children, beloved children." And I remembered the sentence I had

128

chosen as the motto of my ordination: *Et tu puer Propheta altissimi vocaberis*. "And thou, child, shalt be called Prophet of the Highest." And it seemed to me that He was repeating it to me in translation: "You, my boy, my little boy, are going to be called Prophet of the Highest today. But do not fear, I am at your side, and forever. I am with you. *I*."

Never have I felt so alone before God. He could be seen, touched, there, among us. I remembered nothing at this moment, nothing and no one. God was pulsing there in the church and was filling it, to the last corners of life.

We took our places in the chancel and I was assigned a corner; directly in front of me was the center of the altar in which Our Lady of Clemency smiled tenderly, this Virgin who was now an essential part of my existence. How much of me she knew! How many of my fears, my temptations, my falls, my coldnesses, my fervors. With her I had reached the essence of prayer: smiling, and now it was easy for me to talk to her. Therefore, on this morning, I fixed my eyes on hers, waiting for her to speak. And she spoke to me; she told me with her eyes that the hour for joy had come and that soon I would sit on her knees face to face with Christ.

The Bishop vested and the ceremony began like an ordinary Mass. Tonsure was conferred and the subdeacons were ordained and together with them we prostrated ourselves on the floor.

The chapel was narrow and we were so close to each other that we seemed to form a carpet. While the waves of the litany ebbed and flowed, I called to God,

I shouted to Him; it was a dramatic prayer, asking Him to come, to have mercy on us, to deign to hear us. My eyes burned and my hands scratched the carpet, asking Him to come. On my left, Luis was calmer; he could be heard singing perfectly well. I could not sing; my prayers came through between my gasps, in a hoarse and supplicating voice.

The Bishop stood up and his words suddenly calmed my spirit. *That you would vouchsafe to bless these elect,* he sang. And while the choir answered: *We beseech You, hear us,* I felt happines course through my veins as I jubilantly repeated: elect, elect, elect . . .

And for the second time: *That You would vouchsafe to bless and sanctify these elect.* And I, like an echo: elect, elect . . .

And for the third: *That You would vouchsafe to bless, sanctify, and consecrate these elect.* And my eyes opened before the joy and wonder of the enormous word: Elect!

The litany went on and I felt calm. It was He, He, who was choosing us, not men. What tremendous assurance to know that we are His because He has wanted it. He, who knew us just as we were, was calling us, and was calling us for what we were, with all our defects. He would see to what He later did with his "trash".

We rose and while the subdeacons and deacons were being ordained, I looked at the clock so as to fix the hour, the great hour, in my mind.

Now. Now. Now. My heart began to pound just as it had earlier when the Alleluia came into my soul. Dizzily.

The clock: Nine-thirty.

They called us one by one. We answered: *Adsum*. And I listened to my name, the unmistakable call, with the two surnames. And I gave my simple "Present". I had delivered myself into the arms of God.

When we were all in a semi-circle before the Bishop, don Jaime stepped forward and asked him *in the name of the Church* to ordain us priests. And the Bishop answered with the enormous question: *Do you know them to be worthy?*

And the Rector: *As far as human frailty allows to know, I know and I testify that they are worthy of the charge of this office.*

And then the Bishop to all who were present: *Dearly beloved brethren, the captain of a ship as well as the passengers are in the same condition as to safety or danger. Their cause is common, therefore they ought to be of the same mind ... Therefore, whatsoever you know about their lives or character, whatsoever you think of their worthiness, freely make it known.*

And after a few seconds of silence, he turned to us and said.

Dearly beloved sons, you are about to be ordained to the order of the priesthood. Strive to receive it worthily, and having received it, to discharge its duties in a praiseworthy manner. The office of the priest is to offer sacrifice, to bless, to govern, to preach, and to baptize. Truly, it must be with great fear that you ascend to so high a station; and care must be taken that heavenly wisdom, an irreproachable character, and long-continued righteousness shall commend the candidates chosen for it ... The ministers of His church should be perfect in faith and practice, in other words, they should be grounded in the twin virtue of charity, namely, the love of God and the love of neighbor . . . Understand what you do, imitate what you administer. Inasmuch as you celebrate the mystery of the death of the Lord, you should endeavor to mortify in your members all sin and concupiscence. Let your teaching be a spiritual medicine for the people of God and the odor of your lives a delight for the Church of Christ. May you thus build up, by preaching and example, the house, that is, the family of God, so that your promotion may not be a cause of damnation for me, nor the reception of so great an office for you, but rather of reward. May He by His grace grant it to us. Amen.

The Bishop said this long prayer slowly, putting all his heart in every sentence. I scarcely realized what was happening. I knew all this from having read it a hundred thousand times, but then it was impossible for me to control my heart which was crying out: Now, now, now . . .

And the moment came. We stood and lined up two abreast. No, I had never felt closer to God, more alone before with Him, more filled with Him. A terrible certainty that my whole life was changed, that I was now Christ. And when Mariano and I knelt before the Bishop and he imposed his hands on my head, it was as if the floodgates of my soul were opened and the sea of God rushed in overthrowing and felling everything.

And again the deep tears of the morning, tremblingly happy tears which came from the innermost part of my being. And the priests began to pass, one after the other laying their hands on our heads. One, two, three, four, ten, twenty, thirty, sixty, eighty . . . It was a rain of hands. I did not know what to do; I simply cried, feeling so loudly happy . . . On the chasuble which hung from my arm, the wet stain of my tears could be seen; I moved it and let the tears fall on my hands like a harbinger of the holy oil. Finally. Now. Now it's real. I am, I am, I am a priest (1). World without end. No, it is not a job, a position; it is a red sign in the center of being. I thought: ETERNALLY. Although I may be condemned to hell—I trembled—even there I will go on being a priest. We were all now God's strays eternally.

• • •

It was—and I must say and repeat it always—the most complete moment of my life, the moment in which I understood the world, the explanation of things, the marrow of existence itself. Everything about me suddenly made sense. I lovingly pressed my hands together. And I could not doubt, even for an instant, that they were the hands of Christ.

When the priests finished the imposition of hands,

---

(1) Any reader who knows a little theology will realize that, of the two essential parts of the ordination: matter and form, only the matter had been made. I was therefore in error when I thought that it was all complete, because I knew perfectly well that the form had not been pronounced; but I was under the impression that the ordination was over. The moving rite of the imposition of hands seemed more than enough to me to fill the limits of the most mysterious of changes. I understand that this impression of mine was unjustified, but that is how it was, and that is how I tell it.

they stood in a circle around us with their hands held out over our heads—like a roof—and, in the most absolute silence, the Bishop prayed:

Let us pray, dearly beloved brethren, to God, the Father Almighty, that He may multiply heavenly gifts upon these His servants whom He has chosen for the office of the priesthood. May they by His help accomplish what they undertake at His gracious call. Through Christ our Lord. Amen.

Hear us, we beseech You, Lord our God, and pour out upon these Your servants the blessing of the Holy Spirit and the power of grace . . .

We beseech You, almighty Father, invest these Your servants with the dignity of the priesthood. Do You renew in their hearts the spirit of holiness, that they may hold the office, next to ours in importance, which they have received from You, O Lord, and by the example of their lives point out a norm of conduct. May they be prudent fellow laborers of our order; may the pattern of all justice shine forth in them so that, when they will give a good account of the stewardship entrusted to them, they may receive the reward of eternal bliss.

During these prayers my soul began to quiet down. The wave was receding. An infinite peace rushed through my veins. It was the cool of dawn on the beach, the assurance and possession of God. And then a silly happiness came over me; I was filled with freakish laughter; I raised my eyes to the Lady who was smiling from the center of her altar . . . What peace came over me when I looked at her in those moments . . . ! I was the poor

134

little boy who could sleep in her lap without her missing too much the weight of her Son.

After these prayers we again lined up and approached the prelate, one after the other. The Bishop crossed the stole on my breast, saying: *Receive the yoke of the Lord; for His yoke is sweet and His burden light.* And then the chasuble, the back part caught up at my shoulders with two pins: *Receive the priestly vestment, by which charity is signified; for God is powerful to increase unto you charity and perfection of works.*

Now vested with the priestly vestments, we returned to our places and, as we all knelt, the Bishop read this beautiful prayer:

O God, Author of all holiness—I remembered that these sentences were written on a frieze all along the chapel of my seminary—*from whom comes true consecration and the fullness of benediction, do You, O Lord, pour out Your gracious blessing upon these Your servants, upon whom we confer the honor of the priesthood. May they, by gravity of demeanor and strictness of life, prove themselves to be elders, trained according to the principles which Paul set forth to Titus and Timothy. May they keep Your law before their minds day and night, believe what they read, teach what they believe, and practice what they teach. May they show forth in their persons justice, constancy, mercy, fortitude, and all other virtues, be leaders by their example, inspire strength by exhortation, and preserve the gift of their ministry pure and undefiled; may they change by a holy benediction bread and wine into the body and blood of Your Son for the worship of Your people. And having kept their conscience pure and true their faith in never failing charity, may they rise on the day of God's just and final judgment, full of the Holy Spirit, to perfect manhood, in the full measure of the age of Christ. Through the same Jesus Christ, Your Son, our Lord, who lives and reigns with You in the unity of the same Holy Spirit, God forever and ever. Amen.*

So beside myself with joy was I that all this time I did not truly realize what was happening. I said a thousand times, "I am a priest, I am a priest." And this was enough for me.

Then the Bishop knelt and intoned the hymn *Veni Creator*. It was the Church calling to the Holy Spirit to come down to my hands which were going to be anointed a moment later. And it was now that I remembered my family and friends. In the first part of my ordination, I was alone with God, absolutely alone; but now, how could I look at my hands without remembering my parents? How could I touch the ribbon without thinking of my sister who had painted it? I felt myself surrounded by all those who were weeping almost a thousand miles away, bound to them by the same ribbon which in a few seconds was going to join my hands.

Now I really prayed for my hands, now I really remembered their history, now I really asked God to fill them, because I . . . Once again I asked Him to tie me; I asked Him not to let me flounder and lose myself in brooding; I told Him that I was asking it from selfishness and for my own ease, so that things would not be

136

difficult; I told Him it was no sacrifice to surrender Him my freedom.

We drew near. I thought that now I was going to burst out in tears, because my hands have always obsessed me. But no; although I trembled, I had been pervaded by a happiness so great that it did not even leave room for tears. Perhaps I had used them all up at the imposition of hands.

I knelt before the Bishop, holding out my joined palms to him. Dipping his thumb in holy oil he made a large X on them that went from the tip of the index finger of my left hand to the thumb of my right and from the tip of my right index finger to my left palm. Unblinking, I looked at that road of oil which crossed my hands and transformed them for all eternity.

Vouchsafe, O Lord, to consecrate and sanctify these hands . . . that whatsoever they shall bless may be blessed, and whatsoever they shall consecrate be consecrated and sanctified in the name of our Lord Jesus Christ.

I pressed my palms together, feeling how smooth the oil was, and don Jaime bound them together with my sister's ribbon. Among the folds of the knot, I could see the smile of the Virgin my sister had copied onto the ribbon.

And again we knelt before the Bishop: *Receive power to offer sacrifice to God and to celebrate Mass for the living as well as for the dead.*

Afterwards—now it was over, it was all over—we went into the sacristy to wash our hands. (The lot of us could scarcely move.) I washed them with lemon and then with soap. Then they poured out a good shower of cologne on them.

We went out to the altar again. We breathed now with the joy of life fulfilled, new, enormous men. My hands! I looked at them with eyes of amazement, not understanding how what had just happened to them could be possible. Yes, they were the same hands as always, the ones I used to play ball with, the ones with which I took notes and wrote home, the hands that were bored by playing the piano . . . and now—good heavens! —I slowly put them to my lips and kissed my fingertips. No one saw me. Perhaps Our Lady.

The ordination proper had ended; now we would all say Mass together with the Bishop. Thus we all recited the prayers with him aloud. We shouted them wanting each and every word to make sense. The master of ceremonies signalled to us: not so loud, not so loud. And we lowered our voices for a moment, only to begin to shout anew. Yes, we had to put our whole soul in each word and say the prayers feeling them, at least today.

In the *Memento* I offered the Mass for the intentions of the Bishop and then for me, for my new-born priesthood. I prayed later for the eighteen of us; I asked God to make us ordinary priests and without brains, without moodiness. I prayed for my parents, for my brothers and sisters, for my entire family, for all those who during my lifetime were to come in contact with my priesthood.

The Consecration was approaching, the first Consecration in our lives. Each of us in our place, joining our voices to the Bishop's, was going to consecrate the bread and wine that were on the altar. My emotion increased. For a minute, I thought that my tears would keep me from pronouncing the words, but it was all right. It was a serene emotion, a peace and joy which I will never again feel as long as I live. Above all, I felt assurance and immovable faith in what I was going to do. On changing the bread into the Body and the wine into the Blood, transubstantiation was no longer that difficult mystery in the treatises on theology, but something so simple, so at hand . . .

We said the words; we shouted the words:

HOC EST ENIM CORPUS MEUM.

And I could not doubt even for an instant that *I* had worked the miracle of changing into the Body of Christ that Host which the Bishop was raising in his hands. And when he elevated the chalice, trembling, we all adored the miracles of our own lips.

I lifted my eyes to the Blessed Virgin and said to her, "See what a tremendous prank I have played." Yes, without doubt, we had played the most tremendous prank that ever a man has dreamed of.

Yes, mysteries can be seen; one only has to have clear eyes to know that everything is true; one only has to open his eyes to hear all things shout with their mute presence: "Yes, yes, yes, yes, that is God, and you have made Him come with your words."

And so the Mass went on, and at the Communion we achieved the most tangible expression possible of the existence of the Mystical Body. The Bishop gave us Com-

139

munion and each of us received a Host consecrated by the eighteen.

The choir sang: *After today I shall no longer call you servants, but friends, for you know all my secrets. Receive the Holy Spirit.*

And standing we recited the Creed in unison. It was never so easy for me to believe as that morning when my hands were still running with mysteries.

And finally we all passed before the Bishop who again laid on his hands and granted us the overpowering privilege of forgiving sins. They unfolded our chasubles —they had been pinned up until now—as a symbol that all had ended; we promised obedience to the Bishop and received the kiss of peace. Now everything really was over. We were already beginning to forget our past lives and new roads were opening before our souls.

In my corner I cried once more; it was a happy weeping, of one come home, a final, sweet and peaceful weeping.

It was twenty to twelve when we left. Shaking. We had entered not four hours earlier and now the world had been turned topsy-turvy. Now the singing at the beginning was really true: "My beloved children, behold, I am with you, in the very center of your being."

Then in the gallery we all stood in a semicircle around the Bishop while they took many pictures of us—my eyes were still red. And afterwards there was an explosion of happiness. Thousands of arms crushed me, took me back and forth from one place to another; and I could feel nothing as I laid my head on each shoulder for a moment, letting myself be loved and not knowing if I should laugh or cry. And making mistakes on giving the first blessings; and feeling that it was very logical for them to kiss my hands, those hands of God which were ours; and the whole house again bursting into musical Alleluias, and going upstairs and finding on our red counter not 0, but "+1, 2, 3, 4 . . . to eternity."

When I was able to escape from all that happiness, I once again took refuge in the chapel and sat there in a corner saying nothing, thinking nothing, looking only at the place where I had knelt. I had a headache and went up to the terrace to pray. That day the psalms of the Office seemed more exquisite than ever to me, full throughout of symbols. It was a fine day and the golden sun shone on the fronts of the buildings and varnished them with joy. Down in the street, the world went by: cars, cars and buses, men in a hurry, couples locked arm in arm, and children playing with rag balls. I, from above, saw them moving, like little tireless ants; I saw them work, run, go about their business, and I felt that a slight sadness was mixing with my joy. That was why I had become a priest: to teach them to look at heaven, to explain to them that the world is beautiful and that they do not have to rack their brains to find happiness in the world when paradise is within us if we want to look.

At dinner, I scarcely knew what I was eating and that entire afternoon was filled with elementary, inexplicable happiness. Then I went out to buy a ticket for the next day's train to Spain, and the streets seemed strange and unknown to me. I thought, "If a car killed me to-

141

day . . . " And I said, "It doesn't really matter very much to me. My life is complete already." (But I asked God for at least a few days so that I could say my Mass surrounded by all my family.)

I hurriedly packed my bags, throwing the things helter-skelter on top of each other. And so my day ended. It was night when I went up to the terrace to say the rosary: my thanksgiving to the Blessed Mother for the "affair" of the morning.

It was about twelve when I went to my room. All the numbers of the two counters were on my desk.

I got a chair and wrote a number which took up three of the four walls of my room. In 47,613,925,804,127,209 years I would still be a priest.

Once I was in bed, I remembered that I had not written in my diary nor noted down a single line of impressions. I sat down at the desk in my pajamas.

I was exhausted and didn't feel like writing; moreover I knew that there was no possible way of summarizing this 19th day of March.

I took my pen and wrote the page which I now have before me.

March 19, 1953
Twelve fifteen A.M.
O praise the Lord, all ye nations:
Praise Him, all ye peoples.

For His merciful kindness has been great towards us:
and the truth of the Lord endureth forever.
Glory be to the Father, glory to the Son, glory to the
*   Holy Ghost.*
As it was in the beginning, is now and ever shall be, world
*   without end. Amen.*

Back in bed, I looked at the walls of my room and the glorious number. When I had turned out the light, I began to pray.

O God almighty!
O Lord, we praise You.
O Eternal Father, all the earth venerates You.
All the Angels, the heavens and all the angelic Powers.
The Cherubim and Seraphim praise You, crying out as
*   with one voice:*
Holy, Holy, Holy, Lord God of . . .

143

THIS IS MY BODY

I MUST HAVE BEEN VERY PALE WHEN I WENT OUT TO THE ALTAR. Yes, I remember exactly that I wanted to look around the church, but it all seemed blurred and as though full of tears. I thought, "I am going to faint." But I didn't fall; with the strength I felt beneath my feet, I could have stood for hours on end. I remember that I felt hot, that the alb and the chasuble weighed on me, and I had the sensation of not knowing how to walk. When I

145

reached the altar, I think that my uncle lifted the alb while I went up the steps.

The four of us—Facundo, don Victoriano, my uncle, and I—stopped before the altar. Afterwards, they told me that the whole chancel glowed like live coals and that music exploded from the choir. I neither saw nor heard anything.

I said: *In the name of the Father, and of the Son, and of the Holy Ghost.* I spoke slowly, knowing that I was saying something true, that everything which was going to take place there would be in the most holy name of God, and not in mine. I would have liked to repeat it: *In the name of the Father . . .* , but I continued: *I will go unto the altar of God,* and to my right I heard my uncle answer: *Unto God who giveth joy to my youth.* I listened to his strong but slightly broken voice and I understood the tremendous mystery which was joining us there. I noticed that he was shaking; from the height of his 18,000 Masses, he was no doubt remembering his first, as flooded with tears as mine now, and perhaps he thought that one day the same favor would be granted to me. Yes, we do not matter at all; none of us has any worth. The only thing that lasts, the only thing that matters is the priesthood, the gift that men have been transmitting for twenty centuries and which is as new today as it was the first day. I thought, "They are all thinking about the same thing now, about this coincidence which unites us." And I remembered our embrace when I got off the train; I still felt his hand on my head, and his voice: My son . . . "

146

I continued: *Give judgment for me, O God, and distinguish my cause against an unholy people, from unjust and deceitful men deliver me. For Thou art my strength. I shall yet praise Thee upon the harp, O God, my God.* And again: *I will go unto the altar of God. Unto God who giveth joy to my youth.*

And then: *Glory be to the Father and to the Son, and to the Holy Ghost. As it was in the beginning, is now and ever shall be, world without end.* I cried out these words; I wanted them to hear me; I wanted all those in the church to hear me. I would have liked to go out and stop all the people in the street, stop the cars, go into the stores, get on the buses, bang at the doors of the bars, awaken all those who were sleeping, reach all the offices, stop for an instant all the men on earth and force them to give thanks with me, to unite their voice to mine, and shout the name of God at the top of their lungs, because He was great, because He had been good to men and, above all, good to me. *Gloria;* I savored this word as I said it, feeling too dull and small to speak with God and at the same time realizing that He was within reach of my hand.

Then I bent over. "Yes, José Luis, you too are a sinner; if you weren't, you would not be a good priest," Paco had written me in his letter. "A sinner," I said. I would have wanted my soul to be transparent then that they could see how rickety it was, see the filth of my life and all my commonness. I didn't care what they might think. Yes, they consider me a saint now. But I'm not. And they should all know this so as to better understand how unexplainable what is happening to me is: God, who makes no mistakes, before whom there are no good and no bad reputations but only the plain truth, makes me His minister, knowing that my life is far from being the life of a saint. And I remembered the sentence—I think Léon Bloy's—we say a thousand times a day but which I, in that moment, understood was more than just a figure of speech. "Really, the only sorrow in life is that of not being saints." Yes—I bit my lips—God is not going to feel very good now in my hands.

While I was thinking this I slowly said the *Confiteor*. When I finished, the three ministers responded: *May God almighty have mercy upon you, forgive you your sins, and bring you to life everlasting. Amen,* I answered. While they in turn recited the *Confiteor,* I raised my eyes to the Heart of Jesus which stood out above the altar. I saw His open arms and smiled. Yes, perhaps the truly important thing is not for us to be good, but that he is always ready to forgive us . . .

Filled with this assurance, we began the dialogue:

"Thou wilt turn, O God, and bring us to life."

"And Thy people shall rejoice in Thee."

"Show us, O Lord, Thy mercy."

"And grant us Thy salvation."

"O Lord, hear my prayer."

"And let my cry come unto Thee."

When I went up to the altar my friends said they didn't know if the expression my face bore was of laughter or tears. They were four steps that I climbed slowly, knowing that they were definitely bringing me to the great mystery. Now it really had come. Now the thresh-

148

hold was crossed, the veil lifted. I bent over, kissed the altar at the stone which contains the relics of the martyrs, and once again asked God to forgive my sins so that I might celebrate the Holy Sacrifice with purity.

Don Victoriano, the deacon, brought me the thurible and my uncle presented me with incense. Three times I spread it over the coals with the spoon, and a long column of smoke twisted up to the ceiling. And, while I incensed the altar, it seemed to me that I was repeating the words "Glory be to the Father, and to the Son, and to the Holy Ghost." Accompanying the smoke and the noise of the chains, I said, "Oh God, oh God, oh God!"

At the right side of the altar I read the Introit: *I will rejoice in the Lord; and I will rejoice in God my Savior. God is my strength. Rejoice to God our helper. Sing aloud to the God of Jacob.*

At the center I said the *Kyries*. It seemed that once again I was prostrated on the floor, as at the ordination. *Lord, have mercy on us. Christ have mercy on us.* Yes, we again had to ask God to purify us, because what we were going to undertake was very great and we had to go to it with our souls whiter than the vestments which reached our feet.

The choir began to sing the *Gloria*. We sat down. It seemed to me that today also, as in Bethlehem, the angels had come down to organize the celebration. The happiness of the new-born rushed through the pews and through my heart. And I saw it all as a creche of flesh and blood with many shepherds who were coming to see the birth of Christ in the manger of my hands, and down one of

149

those little roads of flour came my mother carrying a baby, a baby who could be a little brother of mine because he was just like me, or perhaps he was me, because my mother called him by my name and he was wearing that blue coat I used to wear the years I studied Latin, and perhaps the city which was shining in the background was not Jerusalem but Astorga and those boys playing ball were my friends and I, and perhaps the palace of Herod was not the palace of Herod but the cathedral or the Bishop's palace or the Town Hall, and those soldiers with mustaches guarding the doors the same ones who came down that July 18th and marched through the streets before my eyes which bulged from their sockets. And that large house looked like the lycée of the Brothers with Julio's house across the street, and the balcony from which his mother sometimes threw down pieces of chocolate, and the little square was the one in front of the Health Center where we so often played ball and from which we occasionally had to run because we had broken a window and don Paco came out shouting; don Paco, with his mustache, who wielded a cane and cursed, and then we were happy we had broken his window because a person who curses deserves everything he gets; and Mocho's house was around the corner, and it was down that street we ran so many days, betting to see who got there first when the important thing was to get there before Brother Rogelio closed the door and marked us absent, and then you had to be bored in Brother Sebastián's class and fill all the margins of your books with drawings and doodles; and when Christmas came you had

150

to put up the crêche and all the houses had to be like ours because we couldn't imagine that in the world there could be houses different from ours and we didn't understand why there wasn't a cathedral in Bethlehem and you had to ask the Brother if the people in Bethlehem were Christians, and on finding out that they weren't you felt like being there and breaking all their windows, but it didn't really matter because you loved all the inhabitants of Bethlehem, at least the shepherds, each of them with a name, like a lifelong friend.

And now, suddenly, you found that you had to prepare another Bethlehem, another crêche, and that you no longer had any imagination, because your childhood was far away; but difficult as it might be you had to make a road down which God could come, and make a cave as best you could, although it were only in the hollow of your hands, and perhaps this is what the angels had come to do, and if I pressed my hands together now maybe I could catch one because there was no doubt that they were working on my hands, doing enormous clearing jobs and afterwards sweeping them and making roads in them so that God could come, and giving them the warmth of a nest so that the Child would not be uncomfortable in them . . .

At the altar I turned to the people: *The Lord be with you.* And I saw that my niece was running down the middle of the church. It gave me the feeling that she was an angel who had been left behind in Bethlehem.

During the Epistle and the Gospel I felt respect when I read the word of God. I seemed to hear the "Remove

151

thy sandals" heard by Moses before the burning bush. As if they were saying to me: Bare your words; cleanse them of the dust of the road, for this earth you tread and these lines you read are holy. "God's will," one of our teachers used to say, "that's what Scripture is." And he added "Nowadays people are dying to read the memoirs of Von Papen or Mussolini and get bored reading the memoirs of God."

After the Gospel I felt very tired and was glad we could sit down during the sermon. I barely remember anything of what was said in it. My soul was a beach that had been too often trodden and each wave erased the preceding one. And so, the words reached my ears, made me tremble for an instant and fled to make way for others. I remember that I cried, that I clenched my fist and that when I looked out into the church I could see my mother crying also. My father was there; to all appearances he was calm, but his eyes seemed lost in space and he gave the impression of not walking this earth. I wasn't calm enough to go on and look at the rest of my family and so I closed my eyes and let the words of the sermon gently come into my soul.

● ● ●

Afterwards we stood, and when I began the Creed my soul went to the catacombs. I remembered the Mass I had heard with a pilgrimage of boys from Madrid three months before. I had spoken to the boys then, and as I talked I shook:

"Look, people have died here. Yes, they have died and not with the high-flown flourish in which we usually drape martyrs. Because the fact is that they were men, men like you and men like me; men who understood that faith was a gamble. It meant risking your skin at any moment. It wasn't that fluffed-up, empty thing we call faith today. I tell you, I'm sorry for that rickety, saccharine piety they talk about so much. Why, faith is something as serious and as human as our own blood, as giving ourselves body and soul to a glorious cause. Smell these walls. They have a taste of humanity, youth and life, and not of rhetoric. We've had enough talk about the era of the martyrs as though it were something from the past. And now," I went on, "we are all going to recite the Creed together. We are going to say it slowly, stopping on each and every one of the words."

I believe in one God, the Father Almighty (a thunder of young voices affirmed it), *Creator of heaven and earth* (of this warm earth we walk, of all the beauty of the city that lies above these cellars); *and in Jesus Christ, His only Son, our Lord* (oh, to think that we say these things as though we were pledging allegiance to the flag!) *who was conceived by the Holy Ghost, born of the Virgin Mary* (You could not be left out of this our creed, white Lady; You, a tenderness that in no way softens the masculine strength of this creed), *suffered under Pontius Pilate* (He suffered, He was a man like you and me), *was crucified, died and was buried* (it has never been easy to die, not even for Him). *He descended into hell; the third day He arose again from the dead* (oh, Your glory, prelude to ours!);

He ascended into heaven; sitteth at the right hand of God, the Father Almighty (waiting for us); *from thence He shall come to judge the living and the dead* (remember this creed then, Judge and Father). *I believe in the Holy Ghost* (I believe, I believe, I believe in Love), *the Holy Catholic Church, the communion of saints, the forgiveness of sins, the resurrection of the body* (of this beautiful body which was not exactly born to be covered with filth), *and life everlasting* (when we will all finally come home). *Amen.*

● ● ●

And now I remembered all of this. I remembered it simply and without effort. I stopped for a moment: But can this be called believing? Faith is believing what we don't see. And I see all this. I am *touching* it. And I turned: *The Lord be with you.*

The Offertory is one of the most beautiful moments of the Mass to me. Holding the paten on the fingertips and lifting the hands in a most beautiful gesture of drawing near to God, there is said this prayer, impressive because of its very simplicity. We call it the *Suscipe*. It is a prayer that eludes all commentary, which has not even one poetic turn, but which does have the terrifying force of being tightly packed with the most disparate and enormous truths.

Receive, O holy Father, almighty and eternal God, this spotless host,

which I, Your unworthy servant,
offer to You, my living and true God,
for my own numberless sins, offenses and failings;
for all here present
and for all faithful Christians, living and dead, that it
   may avail both me and them unto salvation in life
   everlasting.
Amen.

Then, offering the chalice:

We offer You, O Lord,
the chalice of salvation,
imploring Your mercy that it may arise before Your divine
   majesty as a sweet fragrance,
for our salvation and that of all the world.
Amen.
In a humble spirit and contrite in heart,
may we be accepted by You, O Lord,
and may our sacrifice be offered in Your sight this day
   that it be pleasing to You, O Lord God.
Come, almighty Sanctifier and everliving God,
and bless this sacrifice
prepared for the glory of Your holy name.

I said all these words with a sensation of reality
that today amazes me. I knew that each word had its
corresponding object: the sinner was a sinner, and the

155

Eternal was Eternal; the unworthy servant was unworthy and God was a living, real being; the host was spotless and my sins were numberless.

Therefore when I washed my hands I understood how profound that rite was. I knew it was not in vain that the entire first part of the Mass was full of petitions for purity, and if I washed my hands it was because I needed to wash my soul once more so as to enter into the great holiness of mystery if not clean, at least not quite so dirty.

The preface is full of the fluttering of angels' wings. I smiled, understanding that I was returning to my childhood, that my faith in these moments was not the faith of a mature man nor that of a young boy—a faith of clenched teeth and tight fists; it was a normal, simple, effortless faith. I understood that there were angels just as normally as I knew that there were trees or stones or apples. The angels surrounded me and their presence could be as little doubted as the presence of the choir. It was as if I were suddenly going back to fairy tales and the world were really as my mother had told me when I was a child—and it was. At that instant I felt even more intensely than ever the sensation of truth I had clearly tasted in the last few months, this understanding words in a new way, newborn, newly coined words. When a man talks about angels, he uses a special tone of voice, a nuance of commonplaces and worn out words which are enough to convince us that he is not very sure they exist. Now, on the other hand, I found the words to be brand new;

it seemed so natural to me to say that God is worthy of praise and that I who praise Him do it together with an innumerable host of angels and archangels . . .

After the Preface, the missal always has a blank page and then another with a picture of the Crucifixion. This had always given me the impression that you had to stop there, as though it were a door that is opening and you have to look before you walk in lest there be a step beyond it.

And beyond the door there was indeed a step, a terribly high one that had to be climbed: God's step. Everything up until now had been a hallway, but now we were entering the very inner recesses of wonder. I therefore paused a moment before beginning the Canon and I thought: "My friend, it is no longer a question of a little story of yours. It doesn't matter if your heart beats fast or slow. It is a question of something important in the history of the world. Something is going to happen in your hands that will make history change its course. The fact that it is repeated every morning does not stop it from being terribly revolutionary. Yes, friend, you're not burning a lamb to honor the Almighty, or even surrendering Him your life. He is going to come down upon earth to continue that first Good Friday. The fact that He comes to your hands or to someone else's isn't really very important."

I thought: "This happens every morning and I didn't realize it. It happens every morning and only now—now that I touch it—do I realize how astounding this is . . . "

157

I must have spent some time at the *Memento* remembering all my friends. That morning I had opened an enormous pile of letters and they all told me, "Make room for me in your prayers." And now here I was, loaded down with the weight of all my friends; I didn't feel alone. We were all holding out our hands to Christ because, as Gonzalo said, God cannot deny what you ask Him in your first Mass.

The *Communicantes* filled me with joy. I don't know if it was because it was in the name of the Virgin or because of the brotherhood of calling the saints by their names. I said them slowly, remembering each one's story, like that of an old friend.

I remember that about a month ago I wrote a poem which I later tore up because I didn't like it. Now I can only recall one line:

There is a bell which pierces history.

I do not know what came before or after, but I can assure you that this line is not rhetoric and that the bell which rang when I spread my hands over the chalice pierced not only *my* history, but history itself; it was a bell multiplied a thousand, a hundred thousand times every morning, but always it was the same, very important bell. I think if angels could remember things—just one thing —about this world in which we live, they would choose the bell which unceasingly calls them from the four corners of the earth, the bell which never lets them be and

158

makes them tremble day and night. As far as I am concerned, I assure you that I could distinguish its sound from a hundred thousand others. It announced something that was too important to pass over my soul and leave it unmarked.

I now had a strange sensation. Something as if I were seeing a movie and the projectionist had made a mistake and mixed three different pictures together. Where were we? Were we on Calvary as Christ lost His blood drop by drop? Were we at the Last Supper? Or was it I who was officiating at the altar? Why, I even jumbled my words. I said, *"This is my body."* But whose body? *"This is my blood."* What blood, oh God, what blood?. And suddenly I bowed my head and said that it doesn't matter; nothing matters any more because we have entered the forest of miracles and we can no longer be surprised to see a deer talk or know that bread is flesh or that my poor hands are suddenly called holy and venerable.

I felt immense joy, as though in an instant I had been emptied out and a different being put in me, a being that was made of dreams and happiness, perhaps the very Being of Christ. Yes, little one, you have to decide once and for all, my little one; you have to say these words in a completely natural way. Yes, this is your body, that is, the Body of Christ; your body, precisely. Another Christ. Lord, how often I have heard this sentence, feeling that it was something pretty and more or less rhetorical! And now . . .

Come on, take the bread in your hands. Yes, it is still bread, but only for a very few moments now. Take it and say: *The day before He suffered, He took bread into His holy and venerable hands, and with His eyes raised up to heaven, to You, O God, His Father almighty, He blessed, broke and gave it to His disciples saying: Take and eat you of this, for this is My Body.*

I genuflected. Today I cannot tell you if I was shaking, crying or laughing. All that happened in another world which today I am unable to remember. I think the organ played softly in the choir loft, I suppose the bell rang, I imagine that many people wept when I elevated the Host, and I think my hands probably shook as I did it. But all this happened in another world which in those moments was not mine. What really happened in my hands was far beyond anything I can tell you.

Then I elevated the Blood. The Blood! The Blood that redeems and changes the course of history. The Blood that made us children of God. Afraid of spilling It, I gripped the chalice and almost dropped it, so anxious was I to hold it fast. The Blood . . . Why did time again make a mistake and why were the hammers sounding as they had in Bethlehem two thousand years before?

I thought: "What does time matter in the face of mystery? Everything is transfigured and nothing has happened, neither today nor for two thousand years; everything is always the same, today and tomorrow."

After genuflecting before the chalice for the second time, I stopped an instant, as if overwhelmed by the weight of what I had just done. I didn't even have the strength to lift up my arms. I was out of breath. And no, I was not afraid; what I felt was a sensation of crush-

160

ing reality that overpowered me, something totally different from what I had felt up until this moment, something I will never be able to describe because I will never fully understand it.

They almost had to push me to make me continue. And thus I went on: *Unde et memores, Domine . . .*

After a few seconds had gone by, I felt calmer, on the way down. It was as if I had just scaled a high peak and now it were easy to go down to the valley, although I did not know that I had climbed the mountain forever. On making the Sign of the Cross over the Body and the Blood it was like a game; it seemed a tremendous joke to me that my poor hands could bless the Body of Christ. And with this joy, savoring each of the words, I went on to the clear lake of the Communion.

I paused at the edge to ask again—as at the beginning of the Mass—forgiveness for my sins. After the enormous things I had done, I now had a strange feeling again when I spoke of my misery. I therefore said the communion prayers more normally than at the outset of the Mass, although they basically repeated the same thing. I believe that when we ask forgiveness for our sins we really think we are just a little bit like martyrs. It is so beautiful to call oneself a sinner and know you have repented . . . ! I think my repentance now did not have that presumption of feeling myself small; I asked God not to let me abandon Him just as I would ask my mother to clean my nose or something of the sort when I was a child.

Lord, I am not worthy. It seemed a little ridiculous to me to strike my breast when I said it. I thought: In order to say "Lord, I am not a king" I wouldn't need drums and trumpets . . .

I only shook again when I felt the Blood flowing through my veins. Perhaps because I was new at it, I more truly felt God swimming in my veins. The Blood, I repeated . . .

And then came the greatest joy of all, when holding the white Host in my fingers I turned toward the Communion rail where my parents were kneeling.

"*Corpus Domini Nostri,*" I said. Mother, do you remember fourteen years ago when I told you I wanted to be a priest? Twelve years, you thought . . . And now, you see, the day is come. *Corpus Domini Nostri* . . . Mother, it is the Body of Christ that I give you in exchange for my body. I thought: What a paradox! To the woman who made me I give the Body of the One who made her. And afterwards: Do you remember our goodbyes every year when I went back to the seminary? The second year, the third . . . And then: There are seven left and four and two. And then you cried at every first Mass you saw and thought: In nine months, in six months in three . . . And now, Mother, Everything. Now *your* hour is really here. It's worth living if only to see this. Dear Mother, may the Body of Our Lord Jesus Christ keep your soul unto life everlasting. Yes, let the white Host that I have consecrated pass between two rivers of tears, the sweetest tears in your life.

"*Corpus Domini Nostri,*" I said. Father, you do not cry, but your lips are pressed together and you are trying to hold back your emotion; you were always a little in the background at home, a little grey, but we all knew you were there, that your hand would be there when we needed it. You were far from home, but we knew that we lived thanks to your being away. You always used to write, but knowing that now God was among your papers. Don't shake now, Father; open wide your eyes. Yes, it is your son, your youngest child, who is placing the Host on your trembling tongue.

Corpus Domini Nostri. I said it for you too, Paquito, for you who look at me now with infinitely wide eyes, eyes that might seem empty of understanding when they are really full of certainty. May He keep your soul, that soul as tiny and white as I would like mine to be now. Yes, your uncle is giving you Communion, the same one who yesterday afternoon stretched out on the floor to play with you. Yes, with my hands, the same hands that fixed your erector set yesterday. You understand me. Perhaps you understand me better than anybody, because you are the one who is still closest to God.

May the Body of Christ keep your souls, I said, especially all of you, my brother, sister, uncles and aunts, relatives and friends who tremble as you receive Communion from my hands. May Christ be with us world without end.

The rest of the Mass was like a game to me. In an incomprehensible hurry, I rushed through the prayers. Now, when I ask myself why I did it this way, I can give no explanation, but that is what happened. Neither was I aware of it when they came to kiss my hands nor was I conscious of the hugs and handshakes in the sacristy. Per-

163

haps I needed the moment when I could sit in a corner after they had all left and the lights in the church had been turned off one after the other and I was alone without praying, seeing anything or thinking, and scarcely realized that I was crying.

NINE LETTERS RECEIVED

ON THE DAY OF MY ORDINATION AND THE DAY OF MY
FIRST MASS, I received countless letters. I think I hardly
read them. But now they move me strangely when I re-
read them. I am amused to see how each person feels
my priesthood, their different points of view. I am going
to choose some which are interesting to me.

I

Dear Son:

We have received your letter and are glad to learn of your good state of mind on the eve of being ordained to the priesthood. As we mail this letter we are sure that it will reach you on the very day of your ordination and let you know about the feelings which overwhelm us just before the most important thing which has ever happened in our family. It's moving to see how Providence always made our letters arrive at exactly the right moment. Remember how your letters were delivered on time when your brother and sister were married and when your sister Angelines took the habit. That is why I know you will receive this letter precisely on the historic date of the 19th of March which is now so near.

Dear José Luis, if you could only see your mother and me these days. You can't imagine what this means to us. You know we always dreamed of having a son who was a priest, but you'll never realize how we worried as the years went by, afraid that God would not grant us such happiness. Twelve years . . . Can it be truly possible, Lord, that we are going to see it? Now our souls are really at rest. It is near at hand and soon it will be true. We can be satisfied as Christian parents. We were resigned when we offered our first child to heaven and that angel who was not born to live on earth has always been interceding for us there. Later, we offered 50 percent of the children who lived. We gave a son and a daughter to the world so as to perpetuate our family spirit, and to God our other son and daughter. Isn't this also a type of apostolate? Our lives have not been completely sterile, for we hope our children will know how to achieve this task of ours which we decidedly want to be none other than the glory of God.

And see what a wonderful coincidence—do you remember that Crucita said that God protects us *impudently?* At the very moment that you are being ordained your mother will be awarded a special badge as the mother of a priest. In this way we will all be able to tangibly share in the emotions of the date. Your mother well deserves it because she knew how to mould your soul from the time you were a child so that one day you would be a priest.

You tell us that you new priests will give us your first blessing over Vatican radio. God grant that we hear yours, but even though we don't we know it will reach us in exactly the same way that the excited kisses of your parents will reach your consecrated hands.

VALERIANO

My darling son:

Never before have I been as moved as now by the extraordinary favor that God is granting us. Yes, my beloved son, today I received word from my Catholic Action Center telling me that on the 19th I will be awarded the insignia of the mother of a priest. It's coincidence;

167

it's Providence. On the same day that you are ordained a priest of Christ, your mother will wear on her breast the greatest, most moving, most longed-for insignia of all. Yes, my son, thanks to God you are reaching the goal and now you are going to let me recall some details of your boyhood to you. It was mere chance that you were baptized with water from Palestine because your godparents had just come from there; from that August 30, 1930, on we all thought that you would be the chosen one. Oh, but don't think you were an angel, because you were very mischievous and raised all sorts of rumpuses! The years went by and when you were nine and in the Brother's school you were preparing for the Institute. One day you came home and told me that where you really wanted to go was to the seminary. I didn't know what to say to you and very moved I told it to your father. Dad said it would be better for you to go to the Institute for a few years and then we would see if you still had the same idea. But you were stubborn: "I want to go to the seminary now." I described the priest's sacrificing and austere life to you. I talked to you about the seminary which was in a bad way right after the war. I told you about the cold, the food . . . and you with your serious little face answered (it seems that I hear you now), "Mama, I want to go to the seminary." And you entered in October, just after your tenth birthday. That year you still lived at home. I remember it was a very cold winter and every morning when it was time to wake you: Dear God, it has snowed and it's six-thirty A.M. . . . ! But what else could I do? I hurriedly dressed you, put on your cap and your coat and went with you to the seminary (the maids didn't take you one single day), always your mother, and then I would go to seven o'clock Mass in the parish.

How many things I could remind you of about your life in the seminary! The business of your coat, your white sweater, Santibáñez' cassock . . . It would go on forever. How hard it was for me when you went to the seminary in Valladolid and much later when you went off to Rome! But now it's all over and I bear all this with me. And now, what's going to happen? Have you really thought about it, my son? Look, being a priest isn't the same thing as becoming a lawyer or doctor or the like. This is something much more sublime, far above everything in this world. It is simply being another Christ, living, speaking, teaching, preaching and doing everything as He did it. This and only this is what you have to be, my little one. You can well believe that it seems a dream to me. Yes, it is still a dream, but three days from now you will have worked the miracle of all miracles . . . But can it be that those little hands I cared for and washed now have this divine power? But, dear Lord, what have I done for You to grant me this?

I can barely think of the day of your first Mass when you will place Christ in my mouth. I know you will consecrate that Host thinking that it is for Jesus to come to me through you. My son, knowing this I do not understand how there can be so many mothers who begrudge God their sons (you remember the Suárez'). No, my son, I can guarantee you—and I would like to be able to tell it to all mothers on earth—that there is no joy in the world like this one, that feeling yourself a collaborator in that human cathedral which is a priest is the greatest thing of which a mother can dream. It is wonderful enough to give one's children to heaven, but the fact that a child to whom she has given birth is becoming a priest is something beyond all a mother's dreams. Yes, my son, this satisfaction of knowing you are a priest more than repays all the sacrifices of my life as a mother. I bore you in my womb. Blessed be the pains you gave me!

I have nothing more to say. Prepare well for the great day. Beg God to make these days penetrate so deeply into my soul and make me live them so intensely that I forget everything human and see only what they have of the divine.

With all my love,

PEPITA

II

Dear Pepe Luis:

Bless me and give me a hug. I am so stupid that I don't know what to say to you now that you are getting there too. From now on you will understand why, since 5-19-51, I am less interested in science and diplomas and even poetry. I have just finished the third successive retreat and we are still not half way through the Lenten schedule. With grace of God and plenty "Diformil" it will all be done. That, my beloved and *lovable* Pepe Luis, is decidedly what the priesthood is, that beautiful, painful thing that St. Joseph is going to bring you.

If you don't mind, let's talk a little. Look, take advantage of the first month of Masses to make yourself holy forever. Because afterwards come bitterness and grumblings and you feel that your skin is too thick to touch Christ and souls. Believe me, I am ashamed to talk to someone who can still give everything. Thank God, I don't know what an aborted priesthood is. But I can guarantee you that it is infinitely bitter to rob God of even one little crumb a day. Once we said to each other—both leaning out of that well-remembered and familiar window—that the only true sorrow is that of not being a saint. And we weren't just quoting, we really meant it. And then that is the only thing that's left, you'll soon see. I mean, you won't see. Because you simply have to make yourself holy. I ask Jesus for it in an impertinent, gluttonous way and, besides, I give Him reasons that I think will convince Him. Many souls that He himself is giving me are going to ask the same thing of Him: the seventy boys whose confessions I heard after the retreat yesterday afternoon, the three sick women who are going to be operated on at twelve o'clock, the little girl who asked me for an intention for her penances this week, and all the others who come along. You will also be in the prayers of a seven year old girl who spends her week praying for sinners. And after all, we are all sinners; you too, blessed Pepe Luis, because if you weren't you could not be a good priest. An angel sitting in the confessional would be torture for poor men.

You fill me with wonder and respect. And it isn't only your new pontifical character; unfortunately, we see it so often that it even fails to impress us. (Well, what the devil, it does impress me. I'm not that ordinary.) But anyway, I am speaking of José Luis, the presbyter, of all the things you know that I could tell you about but which I won't, and all of it at the service of the great work of redemption that you are beginning. When I see you in your chasuble, I think of the tremendous plans God has in store for you and I am tempted to prophesy. I see you passing among men and crying greatly and daily coming upon God who consoles you. José Luis, my friend, honor no created title or value beyond the ken of your priesthood. You will soon see that in spite of all our longed for humanity the priesthood makes you seem strange to everyone including yourself, and even strange to God when men—you yourself—give you nothing to take Him. Please don't think that these are just words. It is all real and we are too alike for me to believe that the same thing will not happen to you. We also said it before: The virtue of the priest is not specifically purity or chastity; it is faith. Write it down and remember it.

(*Until this point the letter is typed. The rest is hand-written in a diabolic script.*)

172

You may not believe it, but I began this letter a week ago and until now I have literally not had the time to continue. My parish priest has been away for nine days and this coincided with my first week in the hospital. In short, it has been ghastly. Today I am writing you at full speed because at seven o'clock I have to hear confessions at a dormitory and then preach in the Church of the Angustias and, finally, prepare the people who are to be operated on tomorrow. This is sweet and it is brutal. God is wonderful, in spite of everything.

I want to really cry with you tomorrow. My Mass will be totally and exclusively for you and I will try to aim my imagination at the College as assiduously as possible.

Tell all the boys that I love them and I ask God to give them all the best. I will devoutly listen to you on the radio. I commend you to Our Lady.

Pray for me, Pepe Luis. God bless you for your letter. I have not repaid you with this mess of a letter, but I promise to really write you when the paschal alleluias (just you wait and see what sweet Masses) get me out of this whirlwind of eternal truths I am breathing now. Because in spite of so much talk about the Last Things, I'm ready to liven things up. It has been three months since I told a joke or anyone played a trick on me. I feel grownup— don't scorn me—in the worst sense of the word. People only remember priests when something goes wrong. That's why I am using up all my good humor consoling widows and the like. Right now I would enjoy raising the roof, if only for an hour.

That's all for now. Forgive this hodgepodge and have pity on me. I kiss your hands. Goodbye.

Yours,

PACO

III

Dear José Luis:

I have spent a long time thinking about how to begin this letter and I have finally begun just as it came to me. The truth is that I don't know if I ought to write you because perhaps my letter will make you sad. But I am so grateful to you for sending me the invitation that I feel obliged to write you at least a few words.

I don't know, you can't imagine the strange impression I have to think you are a priest. But I beg you not to think it is sadness; it is certainly happiness, but a very odd happiness. I have thought about you often and have cried more than once, but that was a long time ago, at least five years. Now when I remember that summer we met it seems to me that it is something old that happened centuries ago. Look, at heart I am proud to see you become a priest and I would give anything to go to your first Mass. I realize that I shouldn't, but I know that I would cry for joy and that it would be an indelible memory for me.

It is very difficult to tell you what I feel. I think you

will never understand it. It is almost what I would feel for a brother of mine. But so different . . .

No, don't think that I am sad. I'll tell you: I am engaged. Yesterday I told my fiancé I had received your letter, and I said that I had dreamed about you six years ago. He was a little jealous, but then the two of us laughed over it and we have decided that you must marry us. He wants to know what you look like. But you never gave me a picture. It doesn't matter, he will meet you soon; because I hope you will come to town soon to say Mass.

I don't know what I am going to feel when I see you at the altar, and I dream about the moment in which you will give me Communion. I think then we will understand it all, we will understand the ways of God. Yes, only then will we understand. I remember that I cried bitterly when you told me it was all over between us. I think I hated the priesthood then and I even almost stopped going to Communion. But afterwards my anger subsided and I began to view it all more normally. I felt jealous of Christ who had won out over me, but basically I felt happy to have been defeated by such a wonderful enemy. If you had given me up for some other girl I don't think I could have stood it.

I know I shouldn't tell you these things that will probably awaken painful memories on the most moving of all your days. Forgive me and pray for me. I sincerely believe that you still love me but that your love is now purer than ever because it has cost you many sacrifices. Remember me in your first Mass and, when you come, forgive me if I am nervous. You understand.

175

That's all. May you be very happy, as happy as I am now. Pray for me to be happy according to the will of God. You will never be forgotten by . . .

MARISA

IV

Dear Pepe Luis:

I don't know how to begin. The happy news of your first Mass has found me so far away . . . What a shame! And I would have liked to be there to touch your emotion and be with you to feel your innermost palpitations and know what you were saying to Jesus there in your new hands at their debut. We must all pass through your imagination . . . and on elevating the Chalice *pro totius mundi salute* was I there? Do you remember? I am the one who played with you . . . Yes, we prayed together, we studied together, we were together on our walks (because we were the shortest ones in the class), and we even ate our cookies and chocolate bars together.

Last night when, by one of those wonderful coincidences that happen in seminaries, I heard your blessing on the radio it was a fantastic, unexpected joy for me. As soon as I turned it on, there was someone from Madrid and then you. I think I danced for joy and I certainly couldn't go on listening. Look, Pepe Luis, my face has burned from emotion four times in my life; once when something happened in the family, another time when Our Lady of Fatima came to Spain, and another at the definition of the dogma of the Assumption. This has been the fourth time. I never thought it was possible to feel so much joy. I could repeat everything you said, because as soon as you finished I ran to my room to write it down. "I am happy, I am terribly happy because my soul has been filled with God and with the sun. I am happy because on giving you my blessing I know that it is not just another game but that I have God at my side and I can bless you and I bless you in the Name (and you emphasized this word a lot) of the Father and of the Son and of the Holy Ghost."

Hearing your voice at a distance of thousands of miles, that so terribly familiar voice, the same one you used to shout "Kick it hard!" with in our soccer games when we would ruin our shoes in Carbon Square. Do you remember the war years, that morning of the 19th of July when, on our way back from playing at Manjarín, we found the plaza full of miners in pick-up trucks, all of them armed, and we began to run, afraid and not understanding what all that could be? And then the shooting on the next day when they killed Gerardo, and then right after it, peace, but a half-way peace because when we went to play ball we were always missing our center forward and none of our plays would work out.

Then when we would go to the seminary on snow-covered mornings, the streets still not walked on and at six-thirty in the morning and we had to play ball to get warm. And then when we used to throw papers at each other from desk to desk in study hall, not because we had anything to say, but simply to make fun of the watchfulness of the proctor. And the rumpus we would raise when the lights were turned off (or we made them go off, which is not quite the same thing). What a life we had!

And now you see, Pepe Luis, here you are already a priest. And I almost am. After all, what are two years? Fellow, I don't know what to think . . . My mother used to say to me, "Twelve years, twelve years . . ." And then, "Still eight years." And now only two, you might say just the day after tomorrow. It's marvelous. I'm so anxious I can hardly sit still. Every day I say: Tomorrow I will begin to learn how to say Mass. Of course the fact is that I never do, but it's one way of keeping my hopes up while I wait.

Well, José Luis, I won't write you more now because I know you are in no state these days to listen to empty talk and, in view of the wonderful things you are looking forward to now, everything I have written is only idle talk. Be good, and pray for me. I need it very much. God is at my door and I am just as much of a stinker as ever; now that He is so near it really makes me mad to haggle over things with God. Who knows, maybe that's the way it is always going to be and we will always be a little hollow and it will have to be God who fills this trunk of ours. Ask Him to do it for me. I need it, seriously. Meanwhile, here is a big hug from me and a kiss for your anointed hands.

Yours in Christ,
MARIANO

V

My dear friend:

To be sincere, it has never been so difficult for me to write a letter as now. I'm old enough and have been in plenty of scrapes which I have always managed to get out of all right . . . But today it is different. Today means having to talk to you, moved by something in which I do not believe. And when I say "moved" it is because I really am, not because I am "putting it on." My occupation as a writer has often made me do things under false colors, make characters that I hate speak; but, when I did this, I knew that the one who was speaking was not I; he was a character I had created. Today is different. Today I am really shaken by something that goes against all my convictions, something that seems absurd to me.

Moreover there is this fear of hurting you. I understand full well that these days your soul is bared and even the smallest thing can hurt you, and yet I think it is better for you to suffer from my sincerity than from my insincerity. It would be easy for me to write you a polite letter, tell you that "you have chosen the best part" and say, "I wish you a fruitful apostolate." But you would realize perfectly well that it was a *lie*. And you already know that lying is not my strong point.

The news of your first Mass has made me think a lot, and I have reached the conclusion that our friendship is something that has no explanation. Having, as we do, such different ideas, how can we possibly have been able to write each other the letters we have written?

I remember now the first time we met and I am sure that I seemed impolite and discourteous to you then, for it's true that I wasn't really very pleasant, to say the least. But I think it was necessary, because once sides had been a little crudely drawn up, things would go much better. For me, in your first visit you were an "Envoy" from your superiors to "convert" me and it seemed to me that sincerity obligated me to show you that there was nothing you could do, that I was fine where I was—and still am—and did not have the least desire of adopting convictions which I did not feel.

As you see, you have really made very little progress in this respect; I don't say "no progress" because you have done a little: today I think you are all less fanatic; today I think it would be possible for a priest to respect his neighbor's freedom and not hate—because all intransigence is based on hate—those he thinks are in error; today I think it possible to talk about and discuss the most fundamental religious problems without sectarianism, without your insisting on hearing my confession after the first conversation (although the truth is that you are the first priest with whom I have been really friendly).

For my part I also believe I have won out over you a little; I have shown you that not everyone who doesn't think the way you priests do is one of those abominable bogeymen you invent and that one can be honest and work for love among men without being a priest. I think that often what really separates us is not knowing each other rather than the fact that we have different ideas

Now I am happy to read your letters; in them you use no subterfuges to tell me I am in error, and I like that. I see that basically you also want to "convert" me, but you don't do it like the rest; you are tasteful enough not to break off with me because of the fact that we have been arguing for two years and I have not drawn one inch nearer. Another priest after a few attempts would have dubbed me "lost" and forgotten me forever. You have not considered my friendship dangerous for your "soul" and I on my part have not played the role of "tempter" usually assigned to bad men in the dramas of your blessed authors. I do not believe that my letters have ever been demoniacally insidious nor have I attempted to lay skillful traps. I have never tried to "convert" you to my way of thinking. I believe that perhaps the most important thing is for each person to serve God according to the dictates of his own faith. You will say that this is a dreadful theological error, because there is only one true faith; but perhaps deep down you also understand that it is better to be faithful to error than a traitor to the truth, as are so many of those on your side.

Well, I still have not said anything to you of your priesthood. You know that I believe neither in it nor in any of your offices, but I can respect your emotion on receiving it and I think I am even able to say that I share it a little. You are attaining the goal of all your dreams and I who am your friend must rejoice in it, although I believe that all these dreams are empty. Or perhaps not completely empty, for, although I believe that all the rites

are mere illusory fables, I know there will be much love
of God in your soul on that day, and this is something very positive. I beg you not to exclude me from that
love. Pray to God for me; not for me to be converted, but
for me to love Him, which is what—I believe—really
matters. And if you like on that day I will even let you
ask God to convert me. As long as they are motivated by
love, I'll allow you your absurdities.

Very affectionately, your good friend,

E. MARTINEZ MARCOS

VI

Dearest José Luis:

When you receive this letter you will already have seen
the ribbon. Among the brushstrokes you can read many
things that I am not able to tell you now. How often as
I was painting it did I repeat the sentence you wanted me
to write on it: *Cinge me, Domine, et in aeternum ero tecum.* But I changed it a little. Bind me, Lord . . . No, not
me; bind both of us and we will remain with You always.
Your ordination is a new tie that binds us. Will you let
me imagine that I also have a part in your priesthood?
How often your sister has dreamed of this day! You know
full well that my dreams were something more than a
letter. Only God merits this sacrifice of not being at
your side, and it is precisely these sacrifices that we must

182

offer Him, because they are the hardest; He, however, is our Father and He makes me feel very near you. It seems that this distance which sometimes weighs so heavily has suddenly been erased and I feel that you are at my side. Closer than when we were children and used to read the Uncle Fernando stories or played chess and you would always win. We are united by the same ideal. Your life and mine have the same purpose, we are made sad or happy by the same things and we vibrate before the same events. You live *your* priesthood and I live it with you.

St. Thérèse sighed to unite her life to that of a brother who was a priest, and she had to satisfy herself with uniting it to that of some missionaries whom she had never met. While I am no Little Flower, I do have the happiness she never had. You will be a priest!! And in a few days your hands, those hands I see shaking as you hold my letter, will be able to offer the Father together with a large, very white host, another little one, also white, which I place on your paten every day in the morning offering. And when I do it, I am sure that the words of your Mass are not a mere formula; they are an incomprehensible but grandiose reality. "This is My Body, this is My Blood . . . " Then you are not you nor do you belong to yourself. If I unite myself to you, I join myself to Christ and give myself to the souls that God destines to you so that you teach them that they have a Father in heaven and that He is good and He loves them.

I don't know why I remember a phrase they said to us once in a meditation: "Priests are the motor of the Church, nuns the gasoline." From now on I will see to it with my prayers that you never run out of fuel. This is my gift. This is what the ribbon binds. This is how I want to live your priesthood. Are you happy?

Believe me, José Luis, my only thought is this: What is God going to do with my brother? What is he going to do with us? My imagination takes wings and sees you with that first little cassock, the first sacrifices of separation . . . How many things that only He knows which have been forging this day! How well the Lord repays us! What does all that matter in the presence of this infinite joy we have now?

These days I have been receiving many letters from the family and they all tell me the same thing. They are all thinking of you. Crucita and Antonio don't talk to me about the children, it seems that their children have taken second place to your ordination. Mother and Dad . . . they seem mad with joy. How well they are living the grandeur of having a son who is a priest! Really, they are only reaping now what they have already sowed. It is they who have formed our vocations with their hands, because they had done it before in their hearts. What a gift God granted us when He gave them to us for parents! If I didn't know that God is good and loves us and communicates His perfection to His creatures because He is perfect, my intuition would tell me so when I see them. And to think that you with your priesthood can more than repay them all they have done for us . . . !

If I don't find anything to make you understand what I feel when I know that you are almost a priest, what more can I tell you? José Luis, may you be what

184

your dignity demands of you. For while you are a man you can no longer be like other men. Take for your model the One who was God and became a man without ceasing to be God. You are a man and soon you will be Christ without ceasing to be a man, but you must be Christ in such a way that your being a man never prevents the rest from seeing that you are Christ. You need to be very united to Him to do it. Living *your* Mass you will.

On the day of your ordination and of your first Mass be nothing but happy when you think of me. Do not let our separation spoil that day in the least. You know that I am happy, happy, very happy and that feeling you are Christ satisfies me completely and I cannot miss anything.

Many kisses for your hands. Kiss them for me. Don't worry about wetting them with tears because if you were with me now I would do it myself. Give your priestly blessing to your sister who is proud of you and is more united to you than ever.

M. DE LOS ANGELES

VII

My dear friend:

I received your letter the day before yesterday. I can't describe to you how it moved me, with a strange, utterly special emotion. I can't even say if it made me happy or

185

sad; what I can tell you is that I am immensely grateful to you for having thought of me on such a memorable day.

I tell you that I don't know if it made me happy or sad because the very card that gave me the news of your reaching the priesthood was for me the announcement of my failure, if that is what you can call it. How many times I have asked myself if I made a mistake when I left the seminary, if I took the easy way out or if it was a victory! Forgive me if today I cannot think calmly about your attaining the goal without seeing the ghost of my past life which I have so often tried in vain to forget.

I don't know if it is worth telling you about the life I lead now. I am studying Pharmacy and expect to finish next year. I have changed a lot with the years, unfortunately too much in some ways. Possibly I don't deserve you to keep considering me a friend. It is sad to have to speak to you in such a pessimistic fashion. I wouldn't do it if I didn't consider you the best of my friends. It's not because life has been completely adverse to me, but I have seen so many things, so many injustices that there are really times when I feel skeptical and defeated.

The road you have followed is consecrated to God and leads to Him. May He guide you so that you never go astray! When you read my letter, if I am still your friend you can answer with the assurance that you will fill my spirit to overflowing with the deepest satisfaction.

I kiss your hands. Best wishes from . . .

ARTURO ROSALES

186

VIII

Dear *José* Luis:

I have always called you my Benjamin, but today as I write your name I am struck by the "José." Why can't you be my Joseph instead of my Benjamin? Like Jacob I singled you out with my affection among all the other boys in my catechism class thirteen years ago. If they had been able to penetrate my heart, they would have seen you there, dressed in a coat of many colors. I always believed in your dreams, the dreams of an ambitious, a saintly ambitious boy, and I have not been mistaken. To-day the moon and the stars will adore my Joseph. I too could say with the Patriarch: *I shall go and I shall see him and I shall descend to the tomb;* but the Lord keeps my life in order for me to see greater miracles. You are not the symbol of Christ; you are the reality of Christ Himself. God grant that that reality be palpable even to the eyes of the flesh.

Believe me, José Luis, I cried yesterday when I received the news that your ordination is so close at hand. I cried as though a son or a grandson of mine were to be ordained. I feel old and alone, but the joy of seeing your name next to the word "priest" is going to lengthen my life and energy by several years. Look, although I am old, I some-times still think about fatherhood. It is true that being a father of souls is enormously sweet, and hearing myself called father by seven hundred mouths consoles me for the dust there is on my furniture; but there are moments in which my loneliness is very deep and I am tempted to think that our lives are useless . . .

That is why today, José Luis, I feel that you are the fruit of this loneliness of mine, you, my son. I am seventy-one years old, my hair is white and I have three legs, for I can no longer walk without a cane. And now you see that at my age I have the most beautiful of all my children. Will you let me be proud and think that it was I who awoke your vocation and that it was those hours of catechism which made you think about the seminary? I remember as if it were today the day when you said after serving Mass, "It's nice to be a priest." I didn't say anything to you, but the next day when I said my Mass, I was sure that I would see you go up to the altar. But I thought: Twelve years is a long time. And now you see, the time has come. Now I have the feeling that this priesthood of yours would be enough to make my life make sense. I would have done enough by leaving your young blood behind me to keep breaching the gap.

Last night I thought a good deal about these things and I have made a list to conquer the temptation of discouragement. From now on, whenever I start thinking that my life has been useless, I will read it and feel happy. This is my list:

1 priest
7 nuns
17,000 Masses
3,000 weddings
6,000 baptisms

188

    100,000 confessions (approximately)
  1,000,000 sins forgiven (or more)
      5,000 sermons
     17,000 hours of reciting the breviary
     17,000 hours of meditation
      3,000 persons accompanied at the hour of death
            Thousands of letters of spiritual direction
            Thousands of hours of catechism
            Thousands of visits to the sick

I have tossed off this list a bit haphazardly, but I intend to make a complete detailed one. Oh, no, not out of pride. I know what grace is and I have not deserved to say one single Mass, but, what the heck, I have said them and no one can take that from me. Do you know, also, what it means to have made 6,000 Christians, six thousand people who could not have gone to heaven without me?

José Luis, dear José Luis, this is what awaits you. Hours of sadness (yes, many; one cannot deny it) and many more hours of happiness. And above all the satisfaction of having given oneself entirely, of not having anything that is ours; for although we sometimes keep an occasional apple, we have given our tree to God. Look, the priesthood is wonderful. I who am old say it to you. Do you know what it is to baptize a baby and then see him grow and teach him the name of God, and then see their eyes filled with admirable faith when they make their first

Communion; and forgive them their sins (many, you'll soon see), but knowing that they love Christ, the Christ you have shown them, and that when they sin it pains them and it is because life is hard; and then see them build a Christian family and again begin the circle; and you, always lifting, always aiming at heaven? Yes, the priests' heaven must be very large; perhaps we are distributed by parishes up there, finally and truly knowing each other. Now they do not understand, they almost have to be dragged to heaven; but when they understand it up there they are going to cover our feet with tears. Of course we will have to tell them then that it was not us but Christ; but deep down we will be as happy as the mains would be if they realized they bring us the water we drink.

It is night as I write you. All my people are asleep now. Some of them are sinning perhaps, because the flesh is weak, and I am still on duty. More than once they have knocked at my door at this hour of the night: "I was passing by, I saw the light still on and I wondered if you could hear my confession . . . "

One o'clock has struck on the church clock. Now I will repeat as I do every night, with my lips pressed to the Crucifix: *"Tanquam jumentum factus sum apud te* (but fear not, Lord) *sed semper ero tecum* (1)." And tonight I will not sleep from thinking about your ordination eight or ten days from now. And tomorrow in my Mass my words will tremble in a new way and it will seem to me that I am again saying my first Mass (Dear Christ, seventeen thousand of them already!), surrounded by all my

---

(1) "As a little donkey I am at thy side, but I shall always be with thee."

friends and relatives (who now await me in heaven) in the little church in my town, with the young people singing in the choir and the altar covered with lights. I know that I will cry, thanks to you, thanks to Christ who still has mercy on us.

I do not know how to finish. I am terribly anxious for you to come so that I can serve as acolyte at one of your first Masses and remember the time that you used to serve mine fourteen years ago. Ah, then indeed will I be able to say with Abraham: *I shall see thee and I shall descend to the tomb,"* or with Simeon: *"Nunc dimittis servum tuum Domine, secundum verbum tuum in pace, quia viderunt oculi mei salutare tuum. Quod parasti ante faciem omnium populorum. Lumen ad revelationem gentium et gloriam plebis tuae Israel."* (1) My son, do not say that I am a doddering old fool, because it is true that you are my pride and my glory; or perhaps you are not you, but Christ; but all these things are so mysterious that I can no longer tell who it is.

I am going to stop now. I must be in my confessional by six o'clock tomorrow and my poor body is in no condition to stand such strains, but today I needed to get all these things out. Remember me in your first Mass. And be sure that I do not forget you. And now I want to end my letter by calling you brother because, by the time you receive it, the priesthood will have made us equals.

Goodbye, my dear.

Your brother in Christ,

GERARDO

---

(1) "Now dost thou dismiss thy servant, O Lord, according to thy word, in peace; because my eyes have seen thy salvation, which thou hast prepared before the face of all peoples: a light of revelation to the Gentiles, and a glory for the people of Israel." (Luke, 2, 29).

Dear José Luis:

I only wish you one thing: that you always be a Priest, a Priest, a Priest, a Priest, a Priest, a Priest, a Priest, a Priest, a Priest, a Priest. And that afterwards, from far away, very far away, and because there are so many of us who need it, you remember to pray for me; for priests always pray from near, very near. God bless you always as He does today.

Yours,

ANTONIO

I ABSOLVE YOU

(AS I BEGIN TO WRITE THIS CHAPTER *I pause a moment to marvel at the impudence that is needed to write about confession knowing, as I do, so very little about it.*

You, don Gerardo, and not I should write this chapter; you, with your hundred thousand confessions and the million sins you have forgiven . . .

But I think this defect is present in all the pages of this book. Because what can I say about the priesthood? What can I say about the Mass? Perhaps my ingenuousness saves me. Because here it is not a question of dogmatizing, of saying that the priesthood is like this or that it should be like this. It is simply a question of putting these first impressions and this throbbing of the first hours on the table.

Or maybe I should have waited twenty years to write this book. But then perhaps it would not have—oh!—the emotion it does now.)

A few days after my first Mass I again left Spain to renew my everyday life as a student. However, I felt that I lacked something to be a priest in the full sense of the word: hearing confession. Something like the sensation in my ordination when only at the end of the Mass did they unfold our chasubles and give us the power to forgive sins.

Once I was in Italy—and after Easter time when we students at the College would usually help the parish priests in Rome—I did not expect to have the opportunity to do it. But the opportunity came.

It was one night in the middle of May, and therefore very near the examination period. The Rector told us that they had asked him for confessors for a little village near Rome in which they had had a solemn Mission. Almost all of those who offered to go were new priests, and I was one of them.

That afternoon I closed my history books and opened the ones on moral theology which had been closed for three years. As I turned their pages I was filled with fear to think that I no longer knew anything of what I had studied. I was on the verge of going to the Rector to withdraw my name from the list, but I did not have the courage to renounce such a cherished dream. I stayed up studying until two in the morning and entrusted the success of my confessions to God.

During my classes the next morning I don't think I paid attention to any of the lectures. For the first time I felt that I was a father and I saw the faces of all those who were going to come to my confessional. This impression grew in the afternoon when we all sat silently in the bus without venturing to speak, so as not to communicate our fears to each other. I felt closer than ever to mankind —the bus was very crowded; more of a brother to the workers who were perhaps looking at me with eyes fraught with prejudice, to the woman with her basket of fruit, to the chauffeur who opened the communist newspaper as wide as he could before my eyes.

The idea of the blood again came to me. I remember the sentence that somebody once said: "You priests are the ministers of the Blood." And now I was going to distribute it with no less truth than in Communion. I was frightened to think of the tremendous thing I was going to do, once more in the forest of miracles. When I raised my hand, in heaven a page of the book of life was going to be torn. I was not going to perform a more or less beautiful ritual nor console with sweet words full of hope; I was going to fill my hands with miracles of no less importance than curing a sick man or telling the paralytic to walk. Because who but God can forgive sins?

I am obsessed by the idea that we men have lost the

concept of what a miracle really is. We think that a miracle is what we *see* to be useful; a miracle is to hold back a flood, it is a miracle to bring the dead to life, it is a miracle to multiply loaves of bread. But the fact that an offense we have committed against God, which would be enough to make us unhappy for all eternity, is wiped away as though it had never existed, this to us does not seem anything worth ringing bells about. Perhaps it would have been better—I don't know—had God somehow let us see how our sins are erased, something like the hand at the feast of King Balthasar.

The parish priest was waiting for us when we reached the little village at six in the evening. He breathed freely on seeing us and said, "Four, that's fine. You will be needed. I hope there'll be plenty work for all of you tonight."

We went up to the rectory and had a cup of milk. He said, "Now the children will be coming until nine o'clock. At ten we will have Adoration of the Blessed Sacrament for the men and boys and I expect there will be confessions until two when the Mass will begin. Tomorrow morning, the women." He was a pleasant man who considered us a little like sons. The four of us looked at each other rather frightened while we clutched at our rosary in our pockets. We said, "Whenever you say."

The church was small and quite poor, but it had some splendid stained glass windows which gave the church a strange coloring that lent itself to prayer. The parish priest showed them to us with pride. "They are the gift of an American whose son was killed here in the war. They were the stipend for one Mass." He smiled.

He pointed out our confessionals to us. They were narrow and the seats were hard. A hurried sound of steps told us that they had opened the doors, and a flood of children had come into the church. I took a deep breath.

They were two happy hours. At the beginning I had to stammer out my rudimentary Italian, but later everything went smoothly. I can affirm that by the second confession my fears had vanished and I felt unexplicable peace. They came, hurriedly blurted out their sins to me, careful not to forget any of them; you could tell that they had made a list. Then I made my words brief, I attempted to speak their language, and above all wanted to have them leave my confessional happy.

It would be a very sad thing if confession, which was made to forgive, were to make people uneasy.

In short I felt good when it was over. One thing especially made me happy: seeing that they had faith, that they were not going there to meet a requirement, that they went believing that their sins would be forgiven, and they spoke to me just as they would speak to God. This in itself is enough to make one cry for joy.

But it was at night that I really felt I was a confessor. There was a flood of men, boys and youngsters. Today as I think of it in retrospect, I still have the impression that I was on a beach and that the waves came in one after the other to leave me their residue of scum, all the dirt of lowtide that they carried.

I was now seated in a chair and they knelt on a prie-dieu because there were not enough confessionals, and so there we were at close quarters clearly seeing each other's faces Perhaps it was a little harder for them—not much, because they did not know me in the village—but for me it was much better this way. Behind the grating I have the impression of talking to a ghost.

They were simple people, all of them with the very same sins; and one had to speak their language to them, talk about their affairs. I think their sins were not born of malice but of that terribly bored laziness you find in villages, or of that coarse materialism which an everyday way of thinking imparts to earthly things. And raising my hand and seeing that they went away happy and that for a few days at least they would be in God's grace. And explaining to them that confession is something very simple, that the confessor understands because he too is a man and is not going to be shocked by weaknesses whose burden he may very well know himself; and exhorting them not to sleep in sin, to come as soon as anything happened, because then everything will be more beautiful. And seeing that they, yes, especially the boys, understand that an unblemished life is more beautiful, because one can read in their faces the sadness of filthy living.

It was half past two in the morning when I got up from my chair. Worn out from fatigue, but happy; saturated with a joy I cannot define. Loving all those boys and feeling the sadness of seeing them go off, perhaps until the next year, and not being able to follow after them or help them in life, not even help them raise themselves up, for life is hard and the devil does not sleep.

When I went to bed that night and reviewed my day I realized that it was the most complete one in my life. That afternoon a hundred souls had taken a step towards God. And . . . through my hands. I did not feel proud because I knew I was not worthy of that immense gift, but I could not help feeling my soul full and thinking that life was worth living.

At seven in the morning—half asleep—I was again in the confessional, this time to hear the confessions of the women. I can say that it was a totally different thing. Confessing men had brought me closer to God; confessing women brought me close to life, to poor, everyday housework, to the kitchen, to the courtyard. And here one had to give some sense to their lives, fight for them to see God in their pots and pans and not let themselves be consumed by a boredom which would make their lives if not sinful, at least sterile and full of triviality.

And there were also—yes, it must be said—the confessions that left you shaking: the Christian women who knew how to suffer and why they suffered; the men who did not give one inch to selfishness; the old people who spent their lives praying for the world; the young people who kept their purity in the midst of an atmosphere of sin.

And then one had to ask God why he let us sit and they had to kneel when perhaps they were the ones who

199

should have absolved us. And to hear the voice of God laughing, "Stupid, stupid. After all, what does your hand do when it absolves? It is I, you must know it, who forgive. Or maybe you think there is a human being worthy of absolving sins?"

At twelve when I said my Mass and turned around to say *"Dominus vobiscum"* I glanced about the church and felt that somehow it was mine; all those people were in a way my temporal children, my children for the duration of a flash of lightning.

The four of us felt very much like talking on the way back in the bus. We all wanted to tell our impressions which were always the same: happiness, a sentiment of spiritual fatherhood, the desire to begin working seriously. We were all very careful to say absolutely nothing about the contents of the confessions. And you had to forget about wanting to tell of the little mistakes you had made in your Italian that gave rise to funny errors. We knew perfectly well that it could be said, because the seal of confession applies only to sins; but in this matter we all preferred to overdo it and not commit the slightest indiscretion.

The bus now carried us away from the village, and the four of us as if of one mind turned our eyes to the church and engraved it well upon our memories as if it were a little the first parish of our apostleship.

An hour later we came into city traffic, among thous-

200

ands of men who would never be able to understand the exact reason for our joy.

• • •

The second time I heard confessions the circumstances were very different from the first. And now indeed it was unexpected.

When the school year ended I decided to spend a couple of months in a little French town in order to rest and at the same time practice a language whose grammar I know fairly well but in which I had never said four consecutive sentences.

Thus it was that I came to this little French town not very far from Lyon where I am writing these lines. When I arrived and saw the peace of this countryside and the rustic silence of the town, I was very far from imagining what was going to happen to me two days later; and I think that if someone had told me what I am going to relate I would have judged it improbable, just as I am sure half of the readers of this book will judge it.

This is how it happened. At about ten after eight I was peacefully having supper in the tiny dining room of the convent in which I was substituting for the regular chaplain. It was then that the siren blew. A long, doleful sound that was repeated three times and made me halt my spoon in mid-air halfway between the plate and my mouth.

When the errand girl who was serving me my supper came in, in something that resembled French I asked her what was going on as best I could.

"I don't know. It's serious," she said. "Three blasts are serious."

Then the mother superior came in and told me that there had just been a telephone call from the parish church. There had been a railway accident and the parish priest was asking me to accompany him if I could.

Once I was seated beside him in the back of the taxi, after much circumlocution I was finally able to understand that there had been a very serious accident at the outskirts of Chateaubourg, a few miles from Tournon which is where we were.

"Are there many dead?"

"It seems so. Many."

How shall I describe the horrible spectacle, the pile of twisted iron and rails that lay heaped up in the heat of the afternoon that had just ended?

"How did it happen?"

"The 'Michelin' was doing forty-five. A mix-up in the signals sent the freight train down the same track. They didn't see each other on the curve."

The police had put up a barbed-wire barrier to keep the people from going too near the scene of the tragedy. The "Michelin" had four cars which must have been almost completely full of passengers. The engine of the freight train had gone into the first one which encased it like a book cover; inside, it was totally pulverized. The second one was pushed together like an accordion. The third was piled up on top of the other two. The fourth car was intact and had only jumped the track a little.

I felt the blood rush to my head. The long blasts of the locomotive rose above the moans.

"Let's go," the pastor said to me.

I walked almost mechanically. When we reached the barrier the guard stopped us. I heard him speak hurried sentences that I could not understand to my companion. I only heard that they obsessively repeated the words "boiler" and "danger". My companion pressed his lips together and put his chin forward as if trying to control himself. He explained to me:

"It's dangerous. The boiler of the locomotive has been pinned under the first car and it could explode. They're trying to open an escape valve. But it will take them a long time. If it bursts we'll all go up."

"What do we do?"

He didn't answer me. But we both knew that the answer had been given long before. The guard must have understood also because when the two of us began to walk forward at the same instant, as though moved by a spring, he only made a gesture of attempting to stop us.

"My French . . . ," I said.

"Do what you can," he answered. "You don't have to know French to forgive sins."

Yes, I was afraid. My fear was perhaps stronger than myself. The slow groan of the locomotive was like a thorn sinking slowly into my flesh. "We may go up," I repeated. And also, "I absolve you for life eternal . . . "

"Will you give me absolution in case something happens?" I said to him.

I knelt and received God's forgiveness. Then he knelt

and it was my hand that traced the sign of the remission of sins.

We went towards the tragic train. The parish priest of Chateaubourg sighed when he saw us. His face was dirty with coal and blood. He said, "There's nothing we can do in the first car. One of you come with me to the second and the other one climb up to the third."

Through the hole in a window they had just broken open with a hammer, we entered the prison of iron and rubble that was the second car.

"Here, Father, here." I took a deep breath on extending my hand to make the cross of absolution over a face that was as flattened as a loaf of bread. And then over eyes that looked at me from under a seat which two men were trying to break apart with an ax. And over the woman who gripped her stomach trying to hold in the rush of blood that flowed between her legs while saying something I thought I understood: "Father, I was going to Valence to my mother's funeral Mass . . . " And over a girl whose face was hidden by a tragically red veil. And over that blond head separated from an eight year old body . . .

God, God. I said this word many times. And these other disconnected ones: "pray," "forgiveness," "sins." Disconnected words, sentences that never seemed more useless to me beside the stupendous ones *"Ego te absolvo . . . "* And now I knew that it was true, that these few ancient words were the only ones that were of any use at the moment of truth.

And the whistle of the locomotive that went on pier-

204

cing our flesh. "We can go flying through the air at any moment." What was death? What did the word "die" mean now? I had to jump over something that had been a seat and was now a pile of splinters in order to give absolution to a white-haired body before they took it out through the window. And then to the woman buried under a huge heap of suitcases who kept on repeating obsessively, "My daughter, my daughter. Have you seen her? She is a year old, a year old."

It was eleven-thirty at night when the whistle on the locomotive stopped. Next to me a boy wearing a fireman's hat looked at me. We breathed freely.

"They've opened a vent."

"Yes," I said as I put my hands to my forehead. It was then that I felt weak, and I had to reach out for support to keep from falling to the ground. Perhaps my nerves had held me up until then, but now I had no strength, as if I were hollow.

"Father, go out and get a little air. You're going to choke in this hell."

When I got outside I repeated: This hell . . .

A nurse came. I don't know what I answered her nor what she had asked me. She must have realized that I was not French. She pointed to my face. "Blood," she said. I shook my head negatively.

She took me by the hand and pointed out a bucket of water on the road to me. She must have thought me stupid because I stood still without moving. She soaked some bandages in the water and put them to my forehead. I felt the blood gradually return to my head and took away her hand. "Thanks," I said, in Spanish I think, and I submerged my head in the bucket of water.

Then four priests from Valence and two from Saint Peray arrived.

"You aren't needed any more. Sit down here. Rest."

There was a gentle breeze and the night was dark, overcast, as if the entire sky were an enormous cloak of black velvet.

"How many dead are there?"

"Seventeen so far and about ninety injured. But they still haven't been able to get the first car open. They are afraid that they're all dead in there. It's impossible to separate the body from the engine of the freight train. They have gone to Lyon to get a crane to open it like a fan."

I realized then that almost all the people who had surrounded the train at eight were gone. There were about a hundred men left who swarmed around the cars and a couple of dozen nurses who were running from one place to another.

The night became slower. There was an imposing silence. Only from time to time an ambulance left with its cargo of blood, sounding its siren. I sat next to the road, motionless as a statue, without even blinking, as if my pupils were made of marble.

It was about one when the crane from Lyon arrived with a large set of searchlights that—at last—enabled them to see what they were doing.

I think we all feared the moment when they would

open the first car. We saw the hooks go in at both ends, the wheel that slowly, slowly turned; the metal that began to bend, creaking; the windows that burst to pieces; and the tragic load—hands, suitcases, heads, books, raincoats, newspapers, and legs—that went rolling down the embankment at both sides of the track.

I clenched my teeth. I almost brought up my supper. At my side a young nurse uttered a long scream. Then the crane deposited the pile of iron on the road.

It was two in the morning when I again sank back in the seat of the car. My companion sat next to me without saying a word. I believe that the ten minutes it took us to reach our little town were the most intense prayer in my life. I prayed for them, for all the dead—thirty-seven the papers said the next day—as if they had been my brothers. And I felt so close to men . . . I looked at my hands: "They are in heaven now . . . Perhaps someone is in heaven now thanks to these hands . . . "

And it was then when I knew what it was to confess, when the human part of me did not exist, when I was unable to say a word and it was Christ who was using my hands to forgive sins. What did the bit of consolation I gave souls matter? What did the little sermon with which I exhorted them to be better matter before the magnitude of those few words and the sign my hand formed in the air which opened the door to eternal happiness?

EPILOGUE:

ONE HUNDRED AND SEVENTEEN MASSES

Touron, July 15, 1953

Dear Antonio:

You can't imagine my tremendous joy as I begin to write you these lines. When you read them you will *already* be a priest. Do you know that it makes me tremble to say this beautiful word? Antonio, now you will understand many things; you will understand my tears three months ago, you will understand why I was such an awful bore and drove you crazy talking about the priesthood and telling you that you should be ordained soon.

209

To tell the truth, I shake as I write you this letter. I was terribly anxious to write you, I fully intended to tell you a bevy of things and now I don't know what to say nor where to begin or how to talk to you. I think that these days it is perhaps a sin to steal a moment from you, because it's not my words that are going to give you true happiness but the minutes you spend talking with Him and thinking of what You are. You see, I've written "You" with a capital letter, I don't know why. You, you great big philosopher, are no doubt tremendously moved these days on seeing that suddenly life is good for something: for you to realize that the change that has been worked in you is an essential change and not just a costume.

I should like to talk to you now of my experience as a priest, and it seems ridiculous to me. But will you let me be a little high-falutin and say something of these months I have been a priest, of these 117 Masses I have said?

First of all and above all I want to tell you that I am proud of my priesthood and I thank God for it more and more every day. I'm a dog and not a saint or anything even vaguely resembling one. I have to confess to you that I have not made the priesthood shine as I should, but nevertheless it has given me so terribly much happiness that I would not exchange this year for any of the twenty-two that preceded it. I tell you I consider myself a different man, I see the world in a new light and I speak to God in a new way. My Masses . . . no, I no longer shake as I did in the first ones and my vulgarisms and distractions are so numerous that you could never understand them, but

I swear to you that neither would I exchange this half hour in the morning for the sweetest half hour in my life. Because, friend Antonio, the truth is that the Mass—no rhetoric, now—is enough to make you cry for joy. Look, it will happen to you. In a few months you will leave the church dissatisfied with yourself, but not one single day will you be dissatisfied with God when you leave. I assure you that He will put all His flesh on the spit, He will be as close to you as is needed for you to grasp Him and hold out your hand to Him; and although you have a host of distractions there will always be a moment when he sidles into your soul and fills you with enough happiness and juice for the whole rest of the day.

The day after tomorrow I think my Mass will not be as enormous as yours, Antonio; I will not tremble as you will nor will my heart be as large as yours, but the truly marvelous thing is that you, with all your emotion and all your tears will not contribute one iota to your Mass, because He is going to give everything—in your Mass, in mine, and in the Pope's. I don't know what you think of all this, but for me it is a tremendous consolation to know with utter certainty that we don't matter one fig in Mass; no matter how fervid or lukewarm we may be, He will come and everything will occur with the same truth as it happened in Christ's hands on the first Holy Thursday.

This might perhaps seem to excuse our being so common and ordinary, but it is a truth as tall as a mountain. Possibly you think me imprudent to talk of this on the eve of your first Mass, but I am speaking to you for the three months that have passed and for the years that are to come. My brief experience can give you this consolation: Don't worry, my friend; don't fill your mind with questions. Will I always say Mass like this? Will I always be as faithful as now? Such questions in the moments you are going through now would be almost sinful. Decide once and for all that the one important thing is that He has chosen you, that He makes no mistakes and that He is going to come to your hands every morning. It's something else for you to worry about having your hands become cleaner and cleaner every morning; but look, be convinced *a priori* that although they never are, as far as you are concerned, for His stupendous kindness they will always be sufficiently clean. I don't want to throw a wet blanket on your intentions of being holy, but I do want to warn you against a possible pride and angelic dreams to which we have not been called.

Look, before it used to hurt me when people considered us different from other men. Now on the other hand I think that not only are they right, but that in fact the best part of our existence is precisely what there is different about us, what there is in us that is not ours.

Advice? I don't know, I can't give you much. Allow me to tell you just one thing. Open your soul wide these days which may very well be the decisive ones in your life. Afterwards when your grow bourgeois—and sooner or later you will—and when temptation begins—and have no doubt that it will, too—your soul will be so burned and so raw that you will only have to lift up the skin of memory for your priesthood to come to the surface, and it will be your salvation.

And now I think I don't need to tell you how hard I am going to pray for you three days from now. I will say my Mass when you are already dressed in white and awaiting your hour with a madly beating heart. And when I recite the breviary at the bank of the river my heart is often going to fly towards the church in which you will be *being* a priest. And I think that my very hands will fly from me and rest on your head.

Yesterday I left off writing at this point, and today I continue.

I realize that I still haven't explained why I am writing you from this town with such a strange name. And at best you think I have been appointed to a parish. But the name will already have told you that it is a little French town.

And actually, it is. Tournon is a town located between the Rhone and the mountains; the population is about six thousand and there is a marvelous countryside. When the school year ended three weeks ago, I felt tired. And since I don't expect them to make appointments immediately in my diocese I came here to rest, substituting for the chaplain in a convent and at the same time practicing a little French.

This is a girl's school which in the winter must be tremendously chaotic, but it now enjoys an admirable silence. There are only fifteen nuns who tiptoe back and forth and greet me with deep bows. The convent is a large old house that lacks many conveniences, but it does have something I would not trade for all the comfort in the world: a garden on the mountain and a terrace which looks out over the entire valley. Here—I write you in the garden—I spend the whole day walking, reading, and writing.

And I think I ought to tell you that I am writing a book. It's a strange book, about the priesthood. It is called *A Priest Confesses* and I do not know what it is myself. On one hand it seems to be a novel, on the other an autobiography and then again it could be a sermon. There is rather a little of everything in it.

If you ask me why I am writing this book, I will answer that I don't know. Perhaps the reason is the one Scripture gives: *Non possumus quae vidimus et audivimus non loqui* (Acts, iv, 20). You remember when they say it. It's when the Jews have arrested Peter and John and, afraid that the people may rebel, they are released but forbidden to talk. To which Peter and John reply that they cannot keep silent about what they have seen and heard.

Maybe I am going through something like this. This year I have experienced such great things that I believe I would not be capable of keeping silent about them. I think the priesthood means giving oneself completely to all mankind. And each one gives to the measure of his ability, I today, with my writing.

But perhaps the most profound reason for this book is the sadness I feel when I see how little people know of these things. You've seen it a thousand times. In Spanish cathedrals there is an ordination to the priesthood and 120 people attend, strictly the relatives of those who are being ordained. And I sincerely believe that in all the liturgy of the Church there is no more beautiful or impressive ceremony.

Moreover, if you have noticed, all the books which are written about the priesthood nowadays treat it either from an ascetic and therefore abstract point of view, or are written about the priest at work, about the priest in a minor key, as it were. I don't know if I make myself clear. Today all the novels about the priesthood, and there are many, begin with the man's priestly activity. And this is absurd. One cannot know the psychology of a priest without knowing the spiritual earthquake bespoken by ordination. The novelist who studies the priest in his parish will find a stirring about of the ground—resulting from his ordination—that the writer will never be able to fully understand.

Therefore in all these novels man plays a much greater role than God. The more profound ones venture to show man in his relations with God, but in none is God the protagonist through the priest. And I think that after his ordination a priest has much more of the supernatural than the human in him.

As for my book, I am finishing it now. Nevertheless I cannot make up my mind to lay it before the public. You see, regarding us there has been such an abyss of silence, of moral scrutiny, that a priest can no longer tell anything of what he really feels. It is very difficult to restore words to their original purity and strip oneself of the slag of convention. And I have not been sufficiently brave to do it. I have made a confession, but a halfway confession. It is not really I who make it, but a priest in whom I have gathered together all the experiences of my companions with which I am acquainted. There are also some of yours. There is very little fancy or fiction in the book, but not everything that is said in it relates to me. The José Luis of the book is not I. He is a product of adding José Luis + Ricardo + Manuel + Alfredo + Julio + Fidel + etc. This is a book conjointly experienced and almost conjointly written as well. All that is here lived has been lived by us, but not always by me. And even the letters that are transcribed were written to some one of these in the group, but not all to me. I have only had to camouflage the names in order to give greater unity to the story. (I hope that the readers of my book, if it is published, will forgive me this trespass against them).

For those who do not know me, it is not important. They will fabricate for themselves an image that they will believe corresponds to me as I am; but there is not much to be lost by it. And those who know me will rack their brains a bit trying to make out what is mine and what is not. So much the worse for them; they will waste their time to no purpose and will derive no benefit from this book. Because the fact is that I am not I, that it is no concrete person who is confessing. It is simply "a priest." At any rate, I assure you that it is not an easy book and that more than once I have been tempted to bury the manuscript in my desk. But perhaps we have no right to keep so much joy to ourselves.

I ask myself why I write you this. Maybe the answer

is that I feel a need to justify myself to someone. Forgive me and let's not talk about it any more. It seems a crime to me to steal your time today speaking of such trivial matters.

Well, friend Antonio, friend priest. Today I remember your letter: a Priest, a Priest, a Priest . . . Isn't it really wonderful? Yes, we have to be sure of one thing: we men may be this way or that, but God is magnificent. It is a sad mess to think that we all toil to bring what we call human values to perfection when now in the light of these heights they seem so comical and ridiculous. Of course we have to avoid becoming what a friend of mine called the *"nouveaux riches* of God;" but how can we help being rich if we are? Now we need to know it and it is not easy. To know how to give ourselves and above all give to Him. Paco wrote me a few days ago that we priests are in charge of taking souls to Christ and His Mother and that instead we satisfy ourselves with taking Them magnificent piles of words. I answered him that this is exactly the problem: to give souls to Christ and His Mother we have no other means but those very poor piles of words. (The sacraments, too, of course. But they are God's and have nothing to do with us.)

That is about all that I have to say. May I end this letter by reminding you of the definition of the priesthood which the rector used to repeat to us almost every day?

Segregatus a peccatoribus (segregated from sinners) *et excelsior coelis factus* (and raised over the heavens). *Ab hominibus assumptus* (chosen among men) *pro hominibus constitutus* (and constituted to serve men) *ut offerat*

217

dona et sacrificia pro peccatis (in order to offer gifts and sacrifices for sins). *Qui condolere possit* (May he know how to take pity) *quoniam et ipse circumdatus est infirmitate* (because he also is surrounded by infirmity). I will make no comment.

Today you understand all this and much more as it can only be understood on the morning of one's ordination. It is marvelous.

Let me press your hands hard against my lips because finally and forever they are hands worthy of being kissed. I don't know if you remember that I told you months ago that when you were ordained you would see the eighth wonder of the world. You have probably seen it already, closely, but I assure you that in your life there is now beginning a long chain of joys as well as of magnificent sorrows. For only being a priest does one know wonder. In all meanings of the word. My 117 days as a priest attest to it. And like these a thousand, and a hundred thousand and . . . to eternity. Do you remember the counter on the stairs that St. Joseph's morning, the greatest morning in history?

NIHIL OBSTAT: Dr. Eduardo Sánchez, Magister
Valladolid, October 28, 1954
Censor Librorum

IMPRIMATUR: ✠ José *Archbishop of Valladolid*

Attested to by Lic. Modesto Herrero, Canon
Chancellor-Secretary

About the Author

JOSE LUIS MARTIN DESCALZO was born in Madridejos, near Toledo, in 1930. He studied for the priesthood in Astorga, Valladolid, and the Spanish College in Rome, where he was ordained in 1953. Since then he has been alternating between duties as a professor of literature in Valladolid and teaching and studying in Rome. His literary activities began with the founding of the magazine of poetry, *Estría,* while still a seminarian. In 1952 he won the *Insula* Award for the group of sonnets which are included in his collection, *Fábulas con Dios al fondo,* published in 1957. In 1953 his novelette, *Diálogos de cuatro muertos,* was accorded the Naranco award for an outstanding short work of fiction. In 1954 he published this volume, *Un cura se confiesa,* which enjoyed great popularity in Spain and has been translated into most of the major European languages. In 1956 his first full-length novel, *La frontera de Dios,* achieved the coveted Eugenio Nadal Prize—and was subsequently published in the U. S. (by Knopf) as *God's Frontier.* Of it Anne Fremantle said in *The Commonweal:* "A beautifully written novel, arid, monochromatic like a landscape in the Spain from which it comes, but with a really clear intensity in the writing and thinking."

About the Translator

RITA GOLDBERG was born in New York in 1933; attended local schools; graduated from Queen's College and has an M.A. from Middlebury College. After several years in Madrid, and teaching at Queens and Oberlin, she is now Assistant Professor of Spanish at St. Lawrence University in Canton, N.Y.—currently on leave to carry on advanced studies at Brown on a Danforth Foundation Teacher Study Grant. Although Miss Goldberg has translated many shorter pieces from the Spanish, this is her first book length work.